CW00421281

Oscar Fingal O'Flahertie Wills Wilde (16 October 1854 – 30 November 1900) was an Irish poet and playwright. After writing in different forms throughout the 1880s, he became one of London's most popular playwrights in the early 1890s. He is best remembered for his epigrams and plays, his novel The Picture of Dorian Gray, and the circumstances of his criminal conviction for homosexuality, imprisonment, and early death at age 46. Wilde's parents were successful Anglo-Irish intellectuals in Dublin. Their son became fluent in French and German early in life. At university, Wilde read Greats; he proved himself to be an outstanding classicist, first at Trinity College Dublin, then at Oxford. He became known for his involvement in the rising philosophy of aestheticism, led by two of his tutors, Walter Pater and John Ruskin. After university, Wilde moved to London into fashionable cultural and social circles. (Source: Wikipedia)

Literary works:
Ravenna (1878)
Poems (1881)
The Happy Prince and Other Stories (1888)
Lord Arthur Savile's Crime and Other Stories (1891)
A House of Pomegranates (1891)
Intentions (1891)
The Picture of Dorian Gray (1890)
The Soul of Man under Socialism (1891)
Lady Windermere's Fan (1892)
A Woman of No Importance (1893)
An Ideal Husband (1898)
The Importance of Being Earnest (1898)
De Profundis (1905)
The Ballad of Reading Gaol (1898)
The Portrait of Mr. W. H. (1889)

SELECTED POEMS OF
OSCAR WILDE,
SELECTED PROSE OF
OSCAR WILDE
&
SHORTER PROSE PIECES
Oscar Wilde

PRINCE CLASSICS

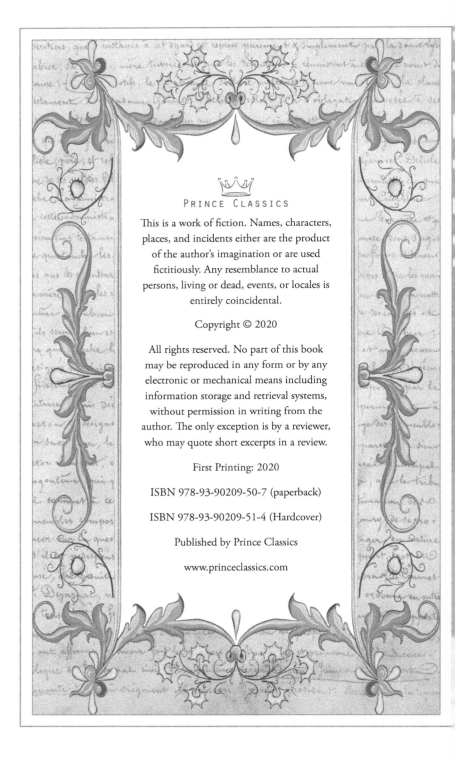

PRINCE CLASSICS

Copyright © 2020

First Printing: 2020

ISBN 978-93-90209-50-7 (paperback)

ISBN 978-93-90209-51-4 (Hardcover)

Published by Prince Classics

www.princeclassics.com

Contents

SELECTED POEMS OF OSCAR WILDE   13

PREFACE   15

NOTE   17

THE BALLAD OF READING GAOL   21

APPENDIX THE BALLAD OF READING GAOL   55

POEMS   **75**

AVE IMPERATRIX   75

TO MY WIFE   82

MAGDALEN WALKS   83

THEOCRITUS   85

SONNETS   **87**

GREECE   87

PORTIA   87

FABIEN DEI FRANCHI   88

PHÈDRE   89

ON HEARING THE DIES IRÆ SUNG IN THE SISTINE CHAPEL   90

AVE MARIA GRATIA PLENA   91

LIBERTATIS SACRA FAMES   91

ROSES AND RUE   92

FROM 'THE GARDEN OF EROS'   96

THE HARLOT'S HOUSE   101

FROM 'THE BURDEN OF ITYS'   103

FLOWER OF LOVE   109

FOOTNOTES   113

SELECTED PROSE OF OSCAR WILDE   **115**

DEDICATION   117

PREFACE   119

HOW THEY STRUCK A CONTEMPORARY   121

THE QUALITY OF GEORGE MEREDITH   122

LIFE THE FALLACIOUS MODEL   123

LIFE THE DISCIPLE   124

LIFE THE PLAGIARIST   125

THE INDISPENSABLE EAST   126

THE INFLUENCE OF THE IMPRESSIONISTS ON CLIMATE   126

AN EXPOSURE OF NATURALISM   128

THOMAS GRIFFITHS WAINEWRIGHT   129

WAINEWRIGHT AT HOBART TOWN   130

CARDINAL NEWMAN AND THE AUTOBIOGRAPHERS   131

ROBERT BROWNING   132

THE TWO SUPREME AND HIGHEST ARTS   133

THE SECRETS OF IMMORTALITY   134

THE CRITIC AND HIS MATERIAL   136

DANTE THE LIVING GUIDE   137

THE LIMITATIONS OF GENIUS   138

WANTED A NEW BACKGROUND   139

WITHOUT FRONTIERS   140

THE POETRY OF ARCHÆOLOGY   141

THE ART OF ARCHÆOLOGY   142

HEROD SUPPLIANT   143

THE TETRARCH'S REMORSE   143

THE TETRARCH'S TREASURE   144

SALOMÉ ANTICIPATES DR. STRAUSS   145

THE YOUNG KING   146

A CORONATION   147

THE KING OF SPAIN   149

A BULL FIGHT 151

THE THRONE ROOM 152

A PROTECTED COUNTRY 154

THE BLACKMAILING OF THE EMPEROR 156

COVENT GARDEN 157

A LETTER FROM MISS JANE PERCY TO HER AUNT 158

THE TRIUMPH OF AMERICAN 'HUMOR' 160

THE GARDEN OF DEATH 161

AN ETON KIT-CAT 163

MRS. ERLYNNE EXERCISES THE PREROGATIVE OF A GRANDMOTHER 165

MOTHERHOOD MORE THAN MARRIAGE 166

THE DAMNABLE IDEAL 167

FROM A REJECTED PRIZE-ESSAY 168

THE POSSIBILITIES OF THE USEFUL 170

THE ARTIST 171

THE DOER OF GOOD 171

THE DISCIPLE 173

THE MASTER 173

THE HOUSE OF JUDGMENT 174

THE TEACHER OF WISDOM 176

WILDE GIVES DIRECTIONS ABOUT 'DE PROFUNDIS' 181

CAREY STREET 183

SORROW WEARS NO MASK 184

VITA NUOVA 185

THE GRAND ROMANTIC 187

CLAPHAM JUNCTION 188

THE BROKEN RESOLUTION 189

DOMESTICITY AT BERNEVAL 190

A VISIT TO THE POPE 192

FOOTNOTES 196

SHORTER PROSE PIECES 199

PHRASES AND PHILOSOPHIES FOR THE USE OF THE YOUNG 201

MRS. LANGTRY AS HESTER GRAZEBROOK 204

SLAVES OF FASHION 206

WOMAN'S DRESS 208

MORE RADICAL IDEAS UPON DRESS REFORM 212

COSTUME 220

THE AMERICAN INVASION 222

SERMONS IN STONES AT BLOOMSBURY THE NEW SCULPTURE ROOM

AT THE BRITISH MUSEUM 226

L'ENVOI 229

About Author 237

NOTABLE WORKS 268

SELECTED POEMS OF
OSCAR WILDE,
SELECTED PROSE OF
OSCAR WILDE
&
SHORTER PROSE PIECES

SELECTED POEMS OF
OSCAR WILDE

PREFACE

It is thought that a selection from Oscar Wilde's early verses may be of interest to a large public at present familiar only with the always popular *Ballad of Reading Gaol*, also included in this volume. The poems were first collected by their author when he was twenty-sex years old, and though never, until recently, well received by the critics, have survived the test of NINE editions. Readers will be able to make for themselves the obvious and striking contrasts between these first and last phases of Oscar Wilde's literary activity. The intervening period was devoted almost entirely to dramas, prose, fiction, essays, and criticism.

ROBERT ROSS

REFORM CLUB,

April 5, 1911.

NOTE

At the end of the complete text will be found a shorter version based on the original draft of the poem. This is included for the benefit of reciters and their audiences who have found the entire poem too long for declamation. I have tried to obviate a difficulty, without officiously exercising the ungrateful prerogatives of a literary executor, by falling back on a text which represents the author's first scheme for a poem—never intended of course for recitation.

ROBERT ROSS

IN MEMORIAM

C. T. W.

Sometimes trooper of

The Royal Horse Guards

Obiit H.M. Prison

Reading, Berkshire

July 7th, 1896

THE BALLAD OF READING GAOL

I

He did not wear his scarlet coat,
  For blood and wine are red,
And blood and wine were on his hands
  When they found him with the dead,
The poor dead woman whom he loved,
  And murdered in her bed.

He walked amongst the Trial Men
  In a suit of shabby grey;
A cricket cap was on his head,
  And his step seemed light and gay;
But I never saw a man who looked
  So wistfully at the day.

I never saw a man who looked
  With such a wistful eye
Upon that little tent of blue
  Which prisoners call the sky,
And at every drifting cloud that went

With sails of silver by.

I walked, with other souls in pain,
　Within another ring,
And was wondering if the man had done
　A great or little thing,
When a voice behind me whispered low,
　'That fellow's got to swing.'

Dear Christ! the very prison walls
　Suddenly seemed to reel,
And the sky above my head became
　Like a casque of scorching steel;
And, though I was a soul in pain,
　My pain I could not feel.

I only knew what hunted thought
　Quickened his step, and why
He looked upon the garish day
　With such a wistful eye;
The man had killed the thing he loved,
　And so he had to die.

Yet each man kills the thing he loves,

By each let this be heard,

Some do it with a bitter look,

Some with a flattering word,

The coward does it with a kiss,

The brave man with a sword!

Some kill their love when they are young,

And some when they are old;

Some strangle with the hands of Lust,

Some with the hands of Gold:

The kindest use a knife, because

The dead so soon grow cold.

Some love too little, some too long,

Some sell, and others buy;

Some do the deed with many tears,

And some without a sigh:

For each man kills the thing he loves,

Yet each man does not die.

He does not die a death of shame

On a day of dark disgrace,

Nor have a noose about his neck,

Nor a cloth upon his face,

Nor drop feet foremost through the floor

    Into an empty space.

He does not sit with silent men

    Who watch him night and day;

Who watch him when he tries to weep,

    And when he tries to pray;

Who watch him lest himself should rob

    The prison of its prey.

He does not wake at dawn to see

    Dread figures throng his room,

The shivering Chaplain robed in white,

    The Sheriff stern with gloom,

And the Governor all in shiny black,

    With the yellow face of Doom.

He does not rise in piteous haste

    To put on convict-clothes,

While some coarse-mouthed Doctor gloats, and notes

    Each new and nerve-twitched pose,

Fingering a watch whose little ticks

    Are like horrible hammer-blows.

He does not know that sickening thirst
 That sands one's throat, before
The hangman with his gardener's gloves
 Slips through the padded door,
And binds one with three leathern thongs,
 That the throat may thirst no more.

He does not bend his head to hear
 The Burial Office read,
Nor, while the terror of his soul
 Tells him he is not dead,
Cross his own coffin, as he moves
 Into the hideous shed.

He does not stare upon the air
 Through a little roof of glass:
He does not pray with lips of clay
 For his agony to pass;
Nor feel upon his shuddering cheek
 The kiss of Caiaphas.

II

Six weeks our guardsman walked the yard,

In the suit of shabby grey:

His cricket cap was on his head,

   And his step seemed light and gay,

But I never saw a man who looked

   So wistfully at the day.

I never saw a man who looked

   With such a wistful eye

Upon that little tent of blue

   Which prisoners call the sky,

And at every wandering cloud that trailed

   Its ravelled fleeces by.

He did not wring his hands, as do

   Those witless men who dare

To try to rear the changeling Hope

   In the cave of black Despair:

He only looked upon the sun,

   And drank the morning air.

He did not wring his hands nor weep,

   Nor did he peek or pine,

But he drank the air as though it held

Some healthful anodyne;

With open mouth he drank the sun

As though it had been wine!

And I and all the souls in pain,

Who tramped the other ring,

Forgot if we ourselves had done

A great or little thing,

And watched with gaze of dull amaze

The man who had to swing.

And strange it was to see him pass

With a step so light and gay,

And strange it was to see him look

So wistfully at the day,

And strange it was to think that he

Had such a debt to pay.

For oak and elm have pleasant leaves

That in the springtime shoot:

But grim to see is the gallows-tree,

With its adder-bitten root,

And, green or dry, a man must die

Before it bears its fruit!

The loftiest place is that seat of grace
    For which all worldlings try:
But who would stand in hempen band
    Upon a scaffold high,
And through a murderer's collar take
    His last look at the sky?

It is sweet to dance to violins
    When Love and Life are fair:
To dance to flutes, to dance to lutes
    Is delicate and rare:
But it is not sweet with nimble feet
    To dance upon the air!

So with curious eyes and sick surmise
    We watched him day by day,
And wondered if each one of us
    Would end the self-same way,
For none can tell to what red Hell
    His sightless soul may stray.

At last the dead man walked no more

Amongst the Trial Men,

And I knew that he was standing up

   In the black dock's dreadful pen,

And that never would I see his face

   In God's sweet world again.

Like two doomed ships that pass in storm

   We had crossed each other's way:

But we made no sign, we said no word,

   We had no word to say;

For we did not meet in the holy night,

   But in the shameful day.

A prison wall was round us both,

   Two outcast men we were:

The world had thrust us from its heart,

   And God from out His care:

And the iron gin that waits for Sin

   Had caught us in its snare.

III

In Debtors' Yard the stones are hard,

   And the dripping wall is high,

So it was there he took the air
    Beneath the leaden sky,
And by each side a Warder walked,
    For fear the man might die.

Or else he sat with those who watched
    His anguish night and day;
Who watched him when he rose to weep,
    And when he crouched to pray;
Who watched him lest himself should rob
    Their scaffold of its prey.

The Governor was strong upon
    The Regulations Act:
The Doctor said that Death was but
    A scientific fact:
And twice a day the Chaplain called,
    And left a little tract.

And twice a day he smoked his pipe,
    And drank his quart of beer:
His soul was resolute, and held
    No hiding-place for fear;

He often said that he was glad
  The hangman's hands were near.

But why he said so strange a thing
  No Warder dared to ask:
For he to whom a watcher's doom
  Is given as his task,
Must set a lock upon his lips,
  And make his face a mask.

Or else he might be moved, and try
  To comfort or console:
And what should Human Pity do
  Pent up in Murderers' Hole?
What word of grace in such a place
  Could help a brother's soul?

With slouch and swing around the ring
  We trod the Fools' Parade!
We did not care: we knew we were
  The Devil's Own Brigade:
And shaven head and feet of lead
  Make a merry masquerade.

We tore the tarry rope to shreds
  With blunt and bleeding nails;
We rubbed the doors, and scrubbed the floors,
  And cleaned the shining rails:
And, rank by rank, we soaped the plank,
  And clattered with the pails.

We sewed the sacks, we broke the stones,
  We turned the dusty drill:
We banged the tins, and bawled the hymns,
  And sweated on the mill:
But in the heart of every man
  Terror was lying still.

So still it lay that every day
  Crawled like a weed-clogged wave:
And we forgot the bitter lot
  That waits for fool and knave,
Till once, as we tramped in from work,
  We passed an open grave.

With yawning mouth the yellow hole

Gaped for a living thing;
The very mud cried out for blood
　To the thirsty asphalte ring:
And we knew that ere one dawn grew fair
　Some prisoner had to swing.

Right in we went, with soul intent
　On Death and Dread and Doom:
The hangman, with his little bag,
　Went shuffling through the gloom:
And each man trembled as he crept
　Into his numbered tomb.

That night the empty corridors
　Were full of forms of Fear,
And up and down the iron town
　Stole feet we could not hear,
And through the bars that hide the stars
　White faces seemed to peer.

He lay as one who lies and dreams
　In a pleasant meadow-land,
The watchers watched him as he slept,

And could not understand

How one could sleep so sweet a sleep

With a hangman close at hand.

But there is no sleep when men must weep

Who never yet have wept:

So we—the fool, the fraud, the knave—

That endless vigil kept,

And through each brain on hands of pain

Another's terror crept.

Alas! it is a fearful thing

To feel another's guilt!

For, right within, the sword of Sin

Pierced to its poisoned hilt,

And as molten lead were the tears we shed

For the blood we had not spilt.

The Warders with their shoes of felt

Crept by each padlocked door,

And peeped and saw, with eyes of awe,

Grey figures on the floor,

And wondered why men knelt to pray

Who never prayed before.

All through the night we knelt and prayed,
    Mad mourners of a corse!
The troubled plumes of midnight were
    The plumes upon a hearse:
And bitter wine upon a sponge
    Was the savour of Remorse.

The grey cock crew, the red cock crew,
    But never came the day:
And crooked shapes of Terror crouched,
    In the corners where we lay:
And each evil sprite that walks by night
    Before us seemed to play.

They glided past, they glided fast,
    Like travellers through a mist:
They mocked the moon in a rigadoon
    Of delicate turn and twist,
And with formal pace and loathsome grace
    The phantoms kept their tryst.

With mop and mow, we saw them go,

Slim shadows hand in hand:

About, about, in ghostly rout

    They trod a saraband:

And the damned grotesques made arabesques,

    Like the wind upon the sand!

With the pirouettes of marionettes,

    They tripped on pointed tread:

But with flutes of Fear they filled the ear,

    As their grisly masque they led,

And loud they sang, and long they sang,

    For they sang to wake the dead.

'Oho!' they cried, 'The world is wide,

    But fettered limbs go lame!

And once, or twice, to throw the dice

    Is a gentlemanly game,

But he does not win who plays with Sin

    In the secret House of Shame.'

No things of air these antics were,

    That frolicked with such glee:

To men whose lives were held in gyves,

And whose feet might not go free,

Ah! wounds of Christ! they were living things,

    Most terrible to see.

Around, around, they waltzed and wound;

    Some wheeled in smirking pairs;

With the mincing step of a demirep

    Some sidled up the stairs:

And with subtle sneer, and fawning leer,

    Each helped us at our prayers.

The morning wind began to moan,

    But still the night went on:

Through its giant loom the web of gloom

    Crept till each thread was spun:

And, as we prayed, we grew afraid

    Of the Justice of the Sun.

The moaning wind went wandering round

    The weeping prison-wall:

Till like a wheel of turning steel

    We felt the minutes crawl:

O moaning wind! what had we done

To have such a seneschal?

At last I saw the shadowed bars,
  Like a lattice wrought in lead,
Move right across the whitewashed wall
  That faced my three-plank bed,
And I knew that somewhere in the world
  God's dreadful dawn was red.

At six o'clock we cleaned our cells,
  At seven all was still,
But the sough and swing of a mighty wing
  The prison seemed to fill,
For the Lord of Death with icy breath
  Had entered in to kill.

He did not pass in purple pomp,
  Nor ride a moon-white steed.
Three yards of cord and a sliding board
  Are all the gallows' need:
So with rope of shame the Herald came
  To do the secret deed.

We were as men who through a fen

Of filthy darkness grope:
We did not dare to breathe a prayer,
Or to give our anguish scope:
Something was dead in each of us,
And what was dead was Hope.

For Man's grim Justice goes its way,
And will not swerve aside:
It slays the weak, it slays the strong,
It has a deadly stride:
With iron heel it slays the strong,
The monstrous parricide!

We waited for the stroke of eight:
Each tongue was thick with thirst:
For the stroke of eight is the stroke of Fate
That makes a man accursed,
And Fate will use a running noose
For the best man and the worst.

We had no other thing to do,
Save to wait for the sign to come:
So, like things of stone in a valley lone,

Quiet we sat and dumb:

But each man's heart beat thick and quick,

    Like a madman on a drum!

With sudden shock the prison-clock

    Smote on the shivering air,

And from all the gaol rose up a wail

    Of impotent despair,

Like the sound that frightened marshes hear

    From some leper in his lair.

And as one sees most fearful things

    In the crystal of a dream,

We saw the greasy hempen rope

    Hooked to the blackened beam,

And heard the prayer the hangman's snare

    Strangled into a scream.

And all the woe that moved him so

    That he gave that bitter cry,

And the wild regrets, and the bloody sweats,

    None knew so well as I:

For he who lives more lives than one

More deaths than one must die.

IV

There is no chapel on the day
   On which they hang a man:
The Chaplain's heart is far too sick,
   Or his face is far too wan,
Or there is that written in his eyes
   Which none should look upon.

So they kept us close till nigh on noon,
   And then they rang the bell,
And the Warders with their jingling keys
   Opened each listening cell,
And down the iron stair we tramped,
   Each from his separate Hell.

Out into God's sweet air we went,
   But not in wonted way,
For this man's face was white with fear,
   And that man's face was grey,
And I never saw sad men who looked
   So wistfully at the day.

I never saw sad men who looked

With such a wistful eye

Upon that little tent of blue

We prisoners called the sky,

And at every careless cloud that passed

In happy freedom by.

But there were those amongst us all

Who walked with downcast head,

And knew that, had each got his due,

They should have died instead:

He had but killed a thing that lived,

Whilst they had killed the dead.

For he who sins a second time

Wakes a dead soul to pain,

And draws it from its spotted shroud,

And makes it bleed again,

And makes it bleed great gouts of blood,

And makes it bleed in vain!

Like ape or clown, in monstrous garb

With crooked arrows starred,

Silently we went round and round

The slippery asphalte yard;

Silently we went round and round,

And no man spoke a word.

Silently we went round and round,

And through each hollow mind

The Memory of dreadful things

Rushed like a dreadful wind,

And Horror stalked before each man,

And Terror crept behind.

The Warders strutted up and down,

And kept their herd of brutes,

Their uniforms were spick and span,

And they wore their Sunday suits,

But we knew the work they had been at,

By the quicklime on their boots.

For where a grave had opened wide,

There was no grave at all:

Only a stretch of mud and sand

By the hideous prison-wall,

And a little heap of burning lime,

That the man should have his pall.

For he has a pall, this wretched man,

Such as few men can claim:

Deep down below a prison-yard,

Naked for greater shame,

He lies, with fetters on each foot,

Wrapt in a sheet of flame!

And all the while the burning lime

Eats flesh and bone away,

It eats the brittle bone by night,

And the soft flesh by day,

It eats the flesh and bone by turns,

But it eats the heart alway.

For three long years they will not sow

Or root or seedling there:

For three long years the unblessed spot

Will sterile be and bare,

And look upon the wondering sky

With unreproachful stare.

They think a murderer's heart would taint
  Each simple seed they sow.
It is not true! God's kindly earth
  Is kindlier than men know,
And the red rose would but blow more red,
  The white rose whiter blow.

Out of his mouth a red, red rose!
  Out of his heart a white!
For who can say by what strange way,
  Christ brings His will to light,
Since the barren staff the pilgrim bore
  Bloomed in the great Pope's sight?

But neither milk-white rose nor red
  May bloom in prison-air;
The shard, the pebble, and the flint,
  Are what they give us there:
For flowers have been known to heal
  A common man's despair.

So never will wine-red rose or white,

Petal by petal, fall

On that stretch of mud and sand that lies

By the hideous prison-wall,

To tell the men who tramp the yard

That God's Son died for all.

Yet though the hideous prison-wall

Still hems him round and round,

And a spirit may not walk by night

That is with fetters bound,

And a spirit may but weep that lies

In such unholy ground,

He is at peace—this wretched man—

At peace, or will be soon:

There is no thing to make him mad,

Nor does Terror walk at noon,

For the lampless Earth in which he lies

Has neither Sun nor Moon.

They hanged him as a beast is hanged:

They did not even toll

A requiem that might have brought

Rest to his startled soul,
But hurriedly they took him out,
  And hid him in a hole.

They stripped him of his canvas clothes,
  And gave him to the flies:
They mocked the swollen purple throat,
  And the stark and staring eyes:
And with laughter loud they heaped the shroud
  In which their convict lies.

The Chaplain would not kneel to pray
  By his dishonoured grave:
Nor mark it with that blessed Cross
  That Christ for sinners gave,
Because the man was one of those
  Whom Christ came down to save.

Yet all is well; he has but passed
  To Life's appointed bourne:
And alien tears will fill for him
  Pity's long-broken urn,
For his mourners will be outcast men,

And outcasts always mourn

V

I know not whether Laws be right,
    Or whether Laws be wrong;
All that we know who lie in gaol
    Is that the wall is strong;
And that each day is like a year,
    A year whose days are long.

But this I know, that every Law
    That men have made for Man,
Since first Man took his brother's life,
    And the sad world began,
But straws the wheat and saves the chaff
    With a most evil fan.

This too I know—and wise it were
    If each could know the same—
That every prison that men build
    Is built with bricks of shame,
And bound with bars lest Christ should see
    How men their brothers maim.

With bars they blur the gracious moon,
And blind the goodly sun:
And they do well to hide their Hell,
For in it things are done
That Son of God nor son of Man
Ever should look upon!

The vilest deeds like poison weeds,
Bloom well in prison-air;
It is only what is good in Man
That wastes and withers there:
Pale Anguish keeps the heavy gate,
And the Warder is Despair.

For they starve the little frightened child
Till it weeps both night and day:
And they scourge the weak, and flog the fool,
And gibe the old and grey,
And some grow mad, and all grow bad,
And none a word may say.

Each narrow cell in which we dwell

Is a foul and dark latrine,
And the fetid breath of living Death
    Chokes up each grated screen,
And all, but Lust, is turned to dust
    In Humanity's machine.

The brackish water that we drink
    Creeps with a loathsome slime,
And the bitter bread they weigh in scales
    Is full of chalk and lime,
And Sleep will not lie down, but walks
    Wild-eyed, and cries to Time.

But though lean Hunger and green Thirst
    Like asp with adder fight,
We have little care of prison fare,
    For what chills and kills outright
Is that every stone one lifts by day
    Becomes one's heart by night.

With midnight always in one's heart,
    And twilight in one's cell,
We turn the crank, or tear the rope,

Each in his separate Hell,

And the silence is more awful far

Than the sound of a brazen bell.

And never a human voice comes near

To speak a gentle word:

And the eye that watches through the door

Is pitiless and hard:

And by all forgot, we rot and rot,

With soul and body marred.

And thus we rust Life's iron chain

Degraded and alone:

And some men curse, and some men weep,

And some men make no moan:

But God's eternal Laws are kind

And break the heart of stone.

And every human heart that breaks,

In prison-cell or yard,

Is as that broken box that gave

Its treasure to the Lord,

And filled the unclean leper's house

With the scent of costliest nard.

Ah! happy they whose hearts can break
    And peace of pardon win!
How else may man make straight his plan
    And cleanse his soul from Sin?
How else but through a broken heart
    May Lord Christ enter in?

And he of the swollen purple throat,
    And the stark and staring eyes,
Waits for the holy hands that took
    The Thief to Paradise;
And a broken and a contrite heart
    The Lord will not despise.

The man in red who reads the Law
    Gave him three weeks of life,
Three little weeks in which to heal
    His soul of his soul's strife,
And cleanse from every blot of blood
    The hand that held the knife.

And with tears of blood he cleansed the hand,

The hand that held the steel:
For only blood can wipe out blood,
    And only tears can heal:
And the crimson stain that was of Cain
    Became Christ's snow-white seal.

VI

In Reading gaol by Reading town
    There is a pit of shame,
And in it lies a wretched man
    Eaten by teeth of flame,
In a burning winding-sheet he lies,
    And his grave has got no name.

And there, till Christ call forth the dead,
    In silence let him lie:
No need to waste the foolish tear,
    Or heave the windy sigh:
The man had killed the thing he loved,
    And so he had to die.

And all men kill the thing they love,
    By all let this be heard,

Some do it with a bitter look,

Some with a flattering word,

The coward does it with a kiss,

The brave man with a sword!

APPENDIX THE BALLAD OF READING GAOL
A VERSION BASED ON THE ORIGINAL DRAFT OF THE POEM

I

He did not wear his scarlet coat,
  For blood and wine are red,
And blood and wine were on his hands
  When they found him with the dead,
The poor dead woman whom he loved,
  And murdered in her bed.

He walked amongst the Trial Men
  In a suit of shabby grey;
A cricket cap was on his head,
  And his step seemed light and gay;
But I never saw a man who looked
  So wistfully at the day.

I never saw a man who looked
  With such a wistful eye
Upon that little tent of blue
  Which prisoners call the sky,

And at every drifting cloud that went
    With sails of silver by.

I walked, with other souls in pain,
    Within another ring,
And was wondering if the man had done
    A great or little thing,
When a voice behind me whispered low,
    'That fellow's got to swing.'

Dear Christ! the very prison walls
    Suddenly seemed to reel,
And the sky above my head became
    Like a casque of scorching steel;
And, though I was a soul in pain,
    My pain I could not feel.

I only knew what hunted thought
    Quickened his step, and why
He looked upon the garish day
    With such a wistful eye;
The man had killed the thing he loved,
    And so he had to die.

Yet each man kills the thing he loves,
  By each let this be heard,
Some do it with a bitter look,
  Some with a flattering word,
The coward does it with a kiss,
  The brave man with a sword!

Some kill their love when they are young,
  And some when they are old;
Some strangle with the hands of Lust,
  Some with the hands of Gold:
The kindest use a knife, because
  The dead so soon grow cold.

Some love too little, some too long,
  Some sell, and others buy;
Some do the deed with many tears,
  And some without a sigh:
For each man kills the thing he loves,
  Yet each man does not die.

He does not die a death of shame

On a day of dark disgrace,

Nor have a noose about his neck,

    Nor a cloth upon his face,

Nor drop feet foremost through the floor

    Into an empty space.

He does not wake at dawn to see

    Dread figures throng his room,

The shivering Chaplain robed in white,

    The Sheriff stern with gloom,

And the Governor all in shiny black,

    With the yellow face of Doom.

He does not rise in piteous haste

    To put on convict-clothes,

While some coarse-mouthed Doctor gloats, and notes

    Each new and nerve-twitched pose,

Fingering a watch whose little ticks

    Are like horrible hammer-blows.

He does not know that sickening thirst

    That sands one's throat, before

The hangman with his gardener's gloves

Slips through the padded door,

And binds one with three leathern thongs,

That the throat may thirst no more.

He does not bend his head to hear

The Burial Office read,

Nor, while the terror of his soul

Tells him he is not dead,

Cross his own coffin, as he moves

Into the hideous shed.

He does not stare upon the air

Through a little roof of glass:

He does not pray with lips of clay

For his agony to pass;

Nor feel upon his shuddering cheek

The kiss of Caiaphas.

II

Six weeks our guardsman walked the yard,

In the suit of shabby grey:

His cricket cap was on his head,

And his step seemed light and gay,

But I never saw a man who looked

So wistfully at the day.

He did not wring his hands nor weep,
    Nor did he peek or pine,
But he drank the air as though it held
    Some healthful anodyne;
With open mouth he drank the sun
    As though it had been wine!

And I and all the souls in pain,
    Who tramped the other ring,
Forgot if we ourselves had done
    A great or little thing,
And watched with gaze of dull amaze
    The man who had to swing.

So with curious eyes and sick surmise
    We watched him day by day,
And wondered if each one of us
    Would end the self-same way,
For none can tell to what red Hell
    His sightless soul may stray.

At last the dead man walked no more

Amongst the Trial Men,

And I knew that he was standing up

  In the black dock's dreadful pen,

And that never would I see his face

  In God's sweet world again.

Like two doomed ships that pass in storm

  We had crossed each other's way:

But we made no sign, we said no word,

  We had no word to say;

For we did not meet in the holy night,

  But in the shameful day.

A prison wall was round us both,

  Two outcast men we were:

The world had thrust us from its heart,

  And God from out His care:

And the iron gin that waits for Sin

  Had caught us in its snare.

III

In Debtors' Yard the stones are hard,

  And the dripping wall is high,

So it was there he took the air

    Beneath the leaden sky,

And by each side a Warder walked,

    For fear the man might die.

Or else he sat with those who watched

    His anguish night and day;

Who watched him when he rose to weep,

    And when he crouched to pray;

Who watched him lest himself should rob

    Their scaffold of its prey.

And twice a day he smoked his pipe,

    And drank his quart of beer:

His soul was resolute, and held

    No hiding-place for fear;

He often said that he was glad

    The hangman's hands were near.

But why he said so strange a thing

    No Warder dared to ask:

For he to whom a watcher's doom

    Is given as his task,

Must set a lock upon his lips,

And make his face a mask.

With slouch and swing around the ring

We trod the Fools' Parade!

We did not care: we knew we were

The Devil's Own Brigade:

And shaven head and feet of lead

Make a merry masquerade.

We tore the tarry rope to shreds

With blunt and bleeding nails;

We rubbed the doors, and scrubbed the floors,

And cleaned the shining rails:

And, rank by rank, we soaped the plank,

And clattered with the pails.

We sewed the sacks, we broke the stones,

We turned the dusty drill:

We banged the tins, and bawled the hymns,

And sweated on the mill:

But in the heart of every man

Terror was lying still.

So still it lay that every day
    Crawled like a weed-clogged wave:
And we forgot the bitter lot
    That waits for fool and knave,
Till once, as we tramped in from work,
    We passed an open grave.

Right in we went, with soul intent
    On Death and Dread and Doom:
The hangman, with his little bag,
    Went shuffling through the gloom:
And each man trembled as he crept
    Into his numbered tomb.

That night the empty corridors
    Were full of forms of Fear,
And up and down the iron town
    Stole feet we could not hear,
And through the bars that hide the stars
    White faces seemed to peer.

But there is no sleep when men must weep

Who never yet have wept:
So we—the fool, the fraud, the knave—
    That endless vigil kept,
And through each brain on hands of pain
    Another's terror crept.

Alas! it is a fearful thing
    To feel another's guilt!
For, right within, the sword of Sin
    Pierced to its poisoned hilt,
And as molten lead were the tears we shed
    For the blood we had not spilt.

The Warders with their shoes of felt
    Crept by each padlocked door,
And peeped and saw, with eyes of awe,
    Grey figures on the floor,
And wondered why men knelt to pray
    Who never prayed before.

The morning wind began to moan,
    But still the night went on:
Through its giant loom the web of gloom

Crept till each thread was spun:

And, as we prayed, we grew afraid

Of the Justice of the Sun.

At last I saw the shadowed bars,

Like a lattice wrought in lead,

Move right across the whitewashed wall

That faced my three-plank bed,

And I knew that somewhere in the world

God's dreadful dawn was red.

At six o'clock we cleaned our cells,

At seven all was still,

But the sough and swing of a mighty wing

The prison seemed to fill,

For the Lord of Death with icy breath

Had entered in to kill.

He did not pass in purple pomp,

Nor ride a moon-white steed.

Three yards of cord and a sliding board

Are all the gallows' need:

So with rope of shame the Herald came

To do the secret deed.

We waited for the stroke of eight:

   Each tongue was thick with thirst:

For the stroke of eight is the stroke of Fate

   That makes a man accursed,

And Fate will use a running noose

   For the best man and the worst.

We had no other thing to do,

   Save to wait for the sign to come:

So, like things of stone in a valley lone,

   Quiet we sat and dumb:

But each man's heart beat thick and quick,

   Like a madman on a drum!

With sudden shock the prison-clock

   Smote on the shivering air,

And from all the gaol rose up a wail

   Of impotent despair,

Like the sound that frightened marshes hear

   From some leper in his lair.

And as one sees most fearful things

In the crystal of a dream,
We saw the greasy hempen rope
  Hooked to the blackened beam,
And heard the prayer the hangman's snare
  Strangled into a scream.

And all the woe that moved him so
  That he gave that bitter cry,
And the wild regrets, and the bloody sweats,
  None knew so well as I:
For he who lives more lives than one
  More deaths than one must die.

IV

There is no chapel on the day
  On which they hang a man:
The Chaplain's heart is far too sick,
  Or his face is far too wan,
Or there is that written in his eyes
  Which none should look upon.

So they kept us close till nigh on noon,
  And then they rang the bell,

And the Warders with their jingling keys
Opened each listening cell,
And down the iron stair we tramped,
Each from his separate Hell.

Out into God's sweet air we went,
But not in wonted way,
For this man's face was white with fear,
And that man's face was grey,
And I never saw sad men who looked
So wistfully at the day.

I never saw sad men who looked
With such a wistful eye
Upon that little tent of blue
We prisoners called the sky,
And at every careless cloud that passed
In happy freedom by.

But there were those amongst us all
Who walked with downcast head,
And knew that, had each got his due,
They should have died instead:

He had but killed a thing that lived,
　　Whilst they had killed the dead.

For he who sins a second time
　　Wakes a dead soul to pain,
And draws it from its spotted shroud,
　　And makes it bleed again,
And makes it bleed great gouts of blood,
　　And makes it bleed in vain!

Like ape or clown, in monstrous garb
　　With crooked arrows starred,
Silently we went round and round
　　The slippery asphalte yard;
Silently we went round and round,
　　And no man spoke a word.

Silently we went round and round,
　　And through each hollow mind
The Memory of dreadful things
　　Rushed like a dreadful wind,
And Horror stalked before each man,
　　And Terror crept behind.

The Warders strutted up and down,
    And kept their herd of brutes,
Their uniforms were spick and span,
    And they wore their Sunday suits,
But we knew the work they had been at,
    By the quicklime on their boots.

For where a grave had opened wide,
    There was no grave at all:
Only a stretch of mud and sand
    By the hideous prison-wall,
And a little heap of burning lime,
    That the man should have his pall.

For he has a pall, this wretched man,
    Such as few men can claim:
Deep down below a prison-yard,
    Naked for greater shame,
He lies, with fetters on each foot,
    Wrapt in a sheet of flame!

For three long years they will not sow

Or root or seedling there:
For three long years the unblessed spot
  Will sterile be and bare,
And look upon the wondering sky
  With unreproachful stare.

They think a murderer's heart would taint
  Each simple seed they sow.
It is not true! God's kindly earth
  Is kindlier than men know,
And the red rose would but blow more red,
  The white rose whiter blow.

Out of his mouth a red, red rose!
  Out of his heart a white!
For who can say by what strange way,
  Christ brings His will to light,
Since the barren staff the pilgrim bore
  Bloomed in the great Pope's sight?

But neither milk-white rose nor red
  May bloom in prison-air;
The shard, the pebble, and the flint,

Are what they give us there:

For flowers have been known to heal

    A common man's despair.

So never will wine-red rose or white,

    Petal by petal, fall

On that stretch of mud and sand that lies

    By the hideous prison-wall,

To tell the men who tramp the yard

    That God's Son died for all.

He is at peace—this wretched man—

    At peace, or will be soon:

There is no thing to make him mad,

    Nor does Terror walk at noon,

For the lampless Earth in which he lies

    Has neither Sun nor Moon.

The Chaplain would not kneel to pray

    By his dishonoured grave:

Nor mark it with that blessed Cross

    That Christ for sinners gave,

Because the man was one of those

Whom Christ came down to save.

Yet all is well; he has but passed

To Life's appointed bourne:

And alien tears will fill for him

Pity's long-broken urn,

For his mourners will be outcast men,

And outcasts always mourn.

POEMS

AVE IMPERATRIX

Set in this stormy Northern sea,
　Queen of these restless fields of tide,
England! what shall men say of thee,
　Before whose feet the worlds divide?

The earth, a brittle globe of glass,
　Lies in the hollow of thy hand,
And through its heart of crystal pass,
　Like shadows through a twilight land,

The spears of crimson-suited war,
　The long white-crested waves of fight,
And all the deadly fires which are
　The torches of the lords of Night.

The yellow leopards, strained and lean,
　The treacherous Russian knows so well,
With gaping blackened jaws are seen

Leap through the hail of screaming shell.

The strong sea-lion of England's wars
    Hath left his sapphire cave of sea,
To battle with the storm that mars
    The stars of England's chivalry.

The brazen-throated clarion blows
    Across the Pathan's reedy fen,
And the high steeps of Indian snows
    Shake to the tread of armèd men.

And many an Afghan chief, who lies
    Beneath his cool pomegranate-trees,
Clutches his sword in fierce surmise
    When on the mountain-side he sees

The fleet-foot Marri scout, who comes
    To tell how he hath heard afar
The measured roll of English drums
    Beat at the gates of Kandahar.

For southern wind and east wind meet

Where, girt and crowned by sword and fire,

England with bare and bloody feet

    Climbs the steep road of wide empire.

O lonely Himalayan height,

    Grey pillar of the Indian sky,

Where saw'st thou last in clanging flight

    Our wingèd dogs of Victory?

The almond-groves of Samarcand,

    Bokhara, where red lilies blow,

And Oxus, by whose yellow sand

    The grave white-turbaned merchants go:

And on from thence to Ispahan,

    The gilded garden of the sun,

Whence the long dusty caravan

    Brings cedar wood and vermilion;

And that dread city of Cabool

    Set at the mountain's scarpèd feet,

Whose marble tanks are ever full

    With water for the noonday heat:

Where through the narrow straight Bazaar
  A little maid Circassian
Is led, a present from the Czar
  Unto some old and bearded Khan,—

Here have our wild war-eagles flown,
  And flapped wide wings in fiery fight;
But the sad dove, that sits alone
  In England—she hath no delight.

In vain the laughing girl will lean
  To greet her love with love-lit eyes:
Down in some treacherous black ravine,
  Clutching his flag, the dead boy lies.

And many a moon and sun will see
  The lingering wistful children wait
To climb upon their father's knee;
  And in each house made desolate

Pale women who have lost their lord
  Will kiss the relics of the slain—

Some tarnished epaulette—some sword—
  Poor toys to soothe such anguished pain.

For not in quiet English fields
  Are these, our brothers, lain to rest,
Where we might deck their broken shields
  With all the flowers the dead love best.

For some are by the Delhi walls,
  And many in the Afghan land,
And many where the Ganges falls
  Through seven mouths of shifting sand.

And some in Russian waters lie,
  And others in the seas which are
The portals to the East, or by
  The wind-swept heights of Trafalgar.

O wandering graves! O restless sleep!
  O silence of the sunless day!
O still ravine! O stormy deep!
  Give up your prey! Give up your prey!

And thou whose wounds are never healed,

Whose weary race is never won,

O Cromwell's England! must thou yield

For every inch of ground a son?

Go! crown with thorns thy gold-crowned head,

Change thy glad song to song of pain;

Wind and wild wave have got thy dead,

And will not yield them back again.

Wave and wild wind and foreign shore

Possess the flower of English land—

Lips that thy lips shall kiss no more,

Hands that shall never clasp thy hand.

What profit now that we have bound

The whole round world with nets of gold,

If hidden in our heart is found

The care that groweth never old?

What profit that our galleys ride,

Pine-forest-like, on every main?

Ruin and wreck are at our side,

Grim warders of the House of Pain.

Where are the brave, the strong, the fleet?

    Where is our English chivalry?

Wild grasses are their burial-sheet,

    And sobbing waves their threnody.

O loved ones lying far away,

    What word of love can dead lips send!

O wasted dust! O senseless clay!

    Is this the end! is this the end!

Peace, peace! we wrong the noble dead

    To vex their solemn slumber so;

Though childless, and with thorn-crowned head,

    Up the steep road must England go,

Yet when this fiery web is spun,

    Her watchmen shall descry from far

The young Republic like a sun

    Rise from these crimson seas of war.

TO MY WIFE

WITH A COPY OF MY POEMS

I can write no stately proem
    As a prelude to my lay;
From a poet to a poem
    I would dare to say.

For if of these fallen petals
    One to you seem fair,
Love will waft it till it settles
    On your hair.

And when wind and winter harden
    All the loveless land,
It will whisper of the garden,
    You will understand.

MAGDALEN WALKS

[*After gaining the Berkeley Gold Medal for Greek at Trinity College, Dublin, in 1874, Oscar Wilde proceeded to Oxford, where he obtained a demyship at Magdalen College. He is the only real poet on the books of that institution.*]

The little white clouds are racing over the sky,
   And the fields are strewn with the gold of the flower of March,
   The daffodil breaks under foot, and the tasselled larch
Sways and swings as the thrush goes hurrying by.

A delicate odour is borne on the wings of the morning breeze,
   The odour of deep wet grass, and of brown new-furrowed earth,
   The birds are singing for joy of the Spring's glad birth,
Hopping from branch to branch on the rocking trees.

And all the woods are alive with the murmur and sound of Spring,
   And the rose-bud breaks into pink on the climbing briar,
   And the crocus-bed is a quivering moon of fire
Girdled round with the belt of an amethyst ring.

And the plane to the pine-tree is whispering some tale of love
   Till it rustles with laughter and tosses its mantle of green,

And the gloom of the wych-elm's hollow is lit with the iris sheen

Of the burnished rainbow throat and the silver breast of a dove.

See! the lark starts up from his bed in the meadow there,

    Breaking the gossamer threads and the nets of dew,

    And flashing adown the river, a flame of blue!

The kingfisher flies like an arrow, and wounds the air.

THEOCRITUS

A VILLANELLE

O singer of Persephone!
  In the dim meadows desolate
Dost thou remember Sicily?

Still through the ivy flits the bee
  Where Amaryllis lies in state;
O Singer of Persephone!

Simætha calls on Hecate
  And hears the wild dogs at the gate;
Dost thou remember Sicily?

Still by the light and laughing sea
  Poor Polypheme bemoans his fate;
O Singer of Persephone!

And still in boyish rivalry
  Young Daphnis challenges his mate;
Dost thou remember Sicily?

Slim Lacon keeps a goat for thee,

For thee the jocund shepherds wait;

O Singer of Persephone!

Dost thou remember Sicily?

SONNETS

GREECE

The sea was sapphire coloured, and the sky

Burned like a heated opal through the air;

   We hoisted sail; the wind was blowing fair

For the blue lands that to the eastward lie.

From the steep prow I marked with quickening eye

   Zakynthos, every olive grove and creek,

   Ithaca's cliff, Lycaon's snowy peak,

And all the flower-strewn hills of Arcady.

The flapping of the sail against the mast,

   The ripple of the water on the side,

   The ripple of girls' laughter at the stern,

The only sounds:—when 'gan the West to burn,

   And a red sun upon the seas to ride,

   I stood upon the soil of Greece at last!

Katakolo.

PORTIA

TO ELLEN TERRY

(Written at the Lyceum Theatre)

I marvel not Bassanio was so bold
　　To peril all he had upon the lead,
　　Or that proud Aragon bent low his head
Or that Morocco's fiery heart grew cold:
For in that gorgeous dress of beaten gold
　　Which is more golden than the golden sun
　　No woman Veronesé looked upon
Was half so fair as thou whom I behold.
Yet fairer when with wisdom as your shield
　　The sober-suited lawyer's gown you donned,
And would not let the laws of Venice yield
　　Antonio's heart to that accursèd Jew—
　　O Portia! take my heart: it is thy due:
I think I will not quarrel with the Bond.

FABIEN DEI FRANCHI

TO MY FRIEND HENRY IRVING

The silent room, the heavy creeping shade,
　　The dead that travel fast, the opening door,
　　The murdered brother rising through the floor,
　　The ghost's white fingers on thy shoulders laid,

88

And then the lonely duel in the glade,

　　The broken swords, the stifled scream, the gore,

　　Thy grand revengeful eyes when all is o'er,—

These things are well enough,—but thou wert made

　　For more august creation! frenzied Lear

　　Should at thy bidding wander on the heath

　　With the shrill fool to mock him, Romeo

For thee should lure his love, and desperate fear

Pluck Richard's recreant dagger from its sheath—

　　Thou trumpet set for Shakespeare's lips to blow!

PHÈDRE

TO SARAH BERNHARDT

How vain and dull this common world must seem

　　To such a One as thou, who should'st have talked

At Florence with Mirandola, or walked

Through the cool olives of the Academe:

Thou should'st have gathered reeds from a green stream

　　For Goat-foot Pan's shrill piping, and have played

　　With the white girls in that Phæacian glade

Where grave Odysseus wakened from his dream.

Ah! surely once some urn of Attic clay

　　Held thy wan dust, and thou hast come again

Back to this common world so dull and vain,

For thou wert weary of the sunless day,

The heavy fields of scentless asphodel,

The loveless lips with which men kiss in Hell.

SONNET

ON HEARING THE DIES IRÆ SUNG IN THE SISTINE CHAPEL

Nay, Lord, not thus! white lilies in the spring,

Sad olive-groves, or silver-breasted dove,

Teach me more clearly of Thy life and love

Than terrors of red flame and thundering.

The hillside vines dear memories of Thee bring:

A bird at evening flying to its nest

Tells me of One who had no place of rest:

I think it is of Thee the sparrows sing.

Come rather on some autumn afternoon,

When red and brown are burnished on the leaves,

And the fields echo to the gleaner's song,

Come when the splendid fulness of the moon

Looks down upon the rows of golden sheaves,

And reap Thy harvest: we have waited long.

AVE MARIA GRATIA PLENA

Was this His coming! I had hoped to see
    A scene of wondrous glory, as was told
    Of some great God who in a rain of gold
Broke open bars and fell on Danae:
Or a dread vision as when Semele
    Sickening for love and unappeased desire
    Prayed to see God's clear body, and the fire
Caught her brown limbs and slew her utterly:
With such glad dreams I sought this holy place,
    And now with wondering eyes and heart I stand
    Before this supreme mystery of Love:
Some kneeling girl with passionless pale face,
    An angel with a lily in his hand,
    And over both the white wings of a Dove.

FLORENCE.

LIBERTATIS SACRA FAMES

Albeit nurtured in democracy,
    And liking best that state republican
    Where every man is Kinglike and no man
Is crowned above his fellows, yet I see,

Spite of this modern fret for Liberty,

    Better the rule of One, whom all obey,

    Than to let clamorous demagogues betray

Our freedom with the kiss of anarchy.

Wherefore I love them not whose hands profane

    Plant the red flag upon the piled-up street

    For no right cause, beneath whose ignorant reign

Arts, Culture, Reverence, Honour, all things fade,

    Save Treason and the dagger of her trade,

    Or Murder with his silent bloody feet.

ROSES AND RUE

(To L. L.)

Could we dig up this long-buried treasure,

    Were it worth the pleasure,

We never could learn love's song,

    We are parted too long.

Could the passionate past that is fled

    Call back its dead,

Could we live it all over again,

    Were it worth the pain!

I remember we used to meet
  By an ivied seat,
And you warbled each pretty word
  With the air of a bird;

And your voice had a quaver in it,
  Just like a linnet,
And shook, as the blackbird's throat
  With its last big note;

And your eyes, they were green and grey
  Like an April day,
But lit into amethyst
  When I stooped and kissed;

And your mouth, it would never smile
  For a long, long while,
Then it rippled all over with laughter
  Five minutes after.

You were always afraid of a shower,
  Just like a flower:

I remember you started and ran

    When the rain began.

I remember I never could catch you,

    For no one could match you,

You had wonderful, luminous, fleet,

    Little wings to your feet.

I remember your hair—did I tie it?

    For it always ran riot—

Like a tangled sunbeam of gold:

    These things are old.

I remember so well the room,

    And the lilac bloom

That beat at the dripping pane

    In the warm June rain;

And the colour of your gown,

    It was amber-brown,

And two yellow satin bows

    From your shoulders rose.

And the handkerchief of French lace

Which you held to your face—

Had a small tear left a stain?

   Or was it the rain?

On your hand as it waved adieu

   There were veins of blue;

In your voice as it said good-bye

   Was a petulant cry,

'You have only wasted your life.'

   (Ah, that was the knife!)

When I rushed through the garden gate

   It was all too late.

Could we live it over again,

   Were it worth the pain,

Could the passionate past that is fled

   Call back its dead!

Well, if my heart must break,

   Dear love, for your sake,

It will break in music, I know,

   Poets' hearts break so.

But strange that I was not told

That the brain can hold

In a tiny ivory cell

God's heaven and hell.

FROM 'THE GARDEN OF EROS'

[In this poem the author laments the growth of materialism in the nineteenth century. He hails Keats and Shelley and some of the poets and artists who were his contemporaries, although his seniors, as the torch-bearers of the intellectual life. Among these are Swinburne, William Morris, Rossetti, and Brune-Jones.]

Nay, when Keats died the Muses still had left

One silver voice to sing his threnody, [128]

But ah! too soon of it we were bereft

When on that riven night and stormy sea

Panthea claimed her singer as her own,

And slew the mouth that praised her; since which time we walk alone,

Save for that fiery heart, that morning star [129]

Of re-arisen England, whose clear eye

Saw from our tottering throne and waste of war

The grand Greek limbs of young Democracy

Rise mightily like Hesperus and bring

The great Republic! him at least thy love hath taught to sing,

And he hath been with thee at Thessaly,

   And seen white Atalanta fleet of foot

In passionless and fierce virginity

   Hunting the tuskèd boar, his honied lute

Hath pierced the cavern of the hollow hill,

And Venus laughs to know one knee will bow before her still.

And he hath kissed the lips of Proserpine,

   And sung the Galilæan's requiem,

That wounded forehead dashed with blood and wine

   He hath discrowned, the Ancient Gods in him

Have found their last, most ardent worshipper,

And the new Sign grows grey and dim before its conqueror.

Spirit of Beauty! tarry with us still,

   It is not quenched the torch of poesy,

The star that shook above the Eastern hill

   Holds unassailed its argent armoury

From all the gathering gloom and fretful fight—

O tarry with us still! for through the long and common night,

Morris, our sweet and simple Chaucer's child,

Dear heritor of Spenser's tuneful reed,

With soft and sylvan pipe has oft beguiled

The weary soul of man in troublous need,

And from the far and flowerless fields of ice

Has brought fair flowers to make an earthly paradise.

We know them all, Gudrun the strong men's bride,

Aslaug and Olafson we know them all,

How giant Grettir fought and Sigurd died,

And what enchantment held the king in thrall

When lonely Brynhild wrestled with the powers

That war against all passion, ah! how oft through summer hours,

Long listless summer hours when the noon

Being enamoured of a damask rose

Forgets to journey westward, till the moon

The pale usurper of its tribute grows

From a thin sickle to a silver shield

And chides its loitering car—how oft, in some cool grassy field

Far from the cricket-ground and noisy eight,

At Bagley, where the rustling bluebells come

Almost before the blackbird finds a mate

And overstay the swallow, and the hum

Of many murmuring bees flits through the leaves,

Have I lain poring on the dreamy tales his fancy weaves,

And through their unreal woes and mimic pain

   Wept for myself, and so was purified,

And in their simple mirth grew glad again;

   For as I sailed upon that pictured tide

The strength and splendour of the storm was mine

Without the storm's red ruin, for the singer is divine;

The little laugh of water falling down

   Is not so musical, the clammy gold

Close hoarded in the tiny waxen town

   Has less of sweetness in it, and the old

Half-withered reeds that waved in Arcady

Touched by his lips break forth again to fresher harmony.

Spirit of Beauty, tarry yet awhile!

   Although the cheating merchants of the mart

With iron roads profane our lovely isle,

   And break on whirling wheels the limbs of Art,

Ay! though the crowded factories beget

The blindworm Ignorance that slays the soul, O tarry yet!

For One at least there is,—He bears his name

    From Dante and the seraph Gabriel,—[136]

Whose double laurels burn with deathless flame

    To light thine altar; He [137] too loves thee well,

Who saw old Merlin lured in Vivien's snare,

And the white feet of angels coming down the golden stair,

Loves thee so well, that all the World for him

    A gorgeous-coloured vestiture must wear,

And Sorrow take a purple diadem,

    Or else be no more Sorrow, and Despair

Gild its own thorns, and Pain, like Adon, be

Even in anguish beautiful;—such is the empery

Which Painters hold, and such the heritage

    This gentle solemn Spirit doth possess,

Being a better mirror of his age

    In all his pity, love, and weariness,

Than those who can but copy common things,

And leave the Soul unpainted with its mighty questionings.

But they are few, and all romance has flown,

And men can prophesy about the sun,

And lecture on his arrows—how, alone,

　Through a waste void the soulless atoms run,

How from each tree its weeping nymph has fled,

And that no more 'mid English reeds a Naiad shows her head.

THE HARLOT'S HOUSE

We caught the tread of dancing feet,

We loitered down the moonlit street,

And stopped beneath the harlot's house.

Inside, above the din and fray,

We heard the loud musicians play

The 'Treues Liebes Herz' of Strauss.

Like strange mechanical grotesques,

Making fantastic arabesques,

The shadows raced across the blind.

We watched the ghostly dancers spin

To sound of horn and violin,

Like black leaves wheeling in the wind.

Like wire-pulled automatons,

Slim silhouetted skeletons

Went sidling through the slow quadrille,

Then took each other by the hand,

And danced a stately saraband;

Their laughter echoed thin and shrill.

Sometimes a clockwork puppet pressed

A phantom lover to her breast,

Sometimes they seemed to try to sing.

Sometimes a horrible marionette

Came out, and smoked its cigarette

Upon the steps like a live thing.

Then, turning to my love, I said,

'The dead are dancing with the dead,

The dust is whirling with the dust.'

But she—she heard the violin,

And left my side, and entered in:

Love passed into the house of lust.

Then suddenly the tune went false,

The dancers wearied of the waltz,

The shadows ceased to wheel and whirl.

And down the long and silent street,

The dawn, with silver-sandalled feet,

Crept like a frightened girl.

FROM 'THE BURDEN OF ITYS'

This English Thames is holier far than Rome,

   Those harebells like a sudden flush of sea

Breaking across the woodland, with the foam

   Of meadow-sweet and white anemone

To fleck their blue waves,—God is likelier there

Than hidden in that crystal-hearted star the pale monks bear!

Those violet-gleaming butterflies that take

   Yon creamy lily for their pavilion

Are monsignores, and where the rushes shake

   A lazy pike lies basking in the sun,

His eyes half shut,—he is some mitred old

Bishop in partibus! look at those gaudy scales all green and gold.

The wind the restless prisoner of the trees

   Does well for Palæstrina, one would say

The mighty master's hands were on the keys

   Of the Maria organ, which they play

When early on some sapphire Easter morn

In a high litter red as blood or sin the Pope is borne

From his dark House out to the Balcony

   Above the bronze gates and the crowded square,

Whose very fountains seem for ecstasy

   To toss their silver lances in the air,

And stretching out weak hands to East and West

In vain sends peace to peaceless lands, to restless nations rest.

Is not yon lingering orange after-glow

   That stays to vex the moon more fair than all

Rome's lordliest pageants! strange, a year ago

   I knelt before some crimson Cardinal

Who bare the Host across the Esquiline,

And now—those common poppies in the wheat seem twice as fine.

The blue-green beanfields yonder, tremulous

   With the last shower, sweeter perfume bring

Through this cool evening than the odorous

   Flame-jewelled censers the young deacons swing,

When the grey priest unlocks the curtained shrine,

And makes God's body from the common fruit of corn and vine.

Poor Fra Giovanni bawling at the Mass

   Were out of tune now, for a small brown bird

Sings overhead, and through the long cool grass

   I see that throbbing throat which once I heard

On starlit hills of flower-starred Arcady,

Once where the white and crescent sand of Salamis meets sea.

Sweet is the swallow twittering on the eaves

   At daybreak, when the mower whets his scythe,

And stock-doves murmur, and the milkmaid leaves

   Her little lonely bed, and carols blithe

To see the heavy-lowing cattle wait

Stretching their huge and dripping mouths across the farmyard gate.

And sweet the hops upon the Kentish leas,

   And sweet the wind that lifts the new-mown hay,

And sweet the fretful swarms of grumbling bees

   That round and round the linden blossoms play;

And sweet the heifer breathing in the stall,

And the green bursting figs that hang upon the red-brick wall,

And sweet to hear the cuckoo mock the spring
  While the last violet loiters by the well,
And sweet to hear the shepherd Daphnis sing
  The song of Linus through a sunny dell
Of warm Arcadia where the corn is gold
And the slight lithe-limbed reapers dance about the wattled fold.

* * * *

It was a dream, the glade is tenantless,
  No soft Ionian laughter moves the air,
The Thames creeps on in sluggish leadenness,
  And from the copse left desolate and bare
Fled is young Bacchus with his revelry,
Yet still from Nuneham wood there comes that thrilling melody

So sad, that one might think a human heart
  Brake in each separate note, a quality
Which music sometimes has, being the Art
  Which is most nigh to tears and memory;
Poor mourning Philomel, what dost thou fear?
Thy sister doth not haunt these fields, Pandion is not here,

Here is no cruel Lord with murderous blade,

No woven web of bloody heraldries,

But mossy dells for roving comrades made,

   Warm valleys where the tired student lies

With half-shut book, and many a winding walk

Where rustic lovers stray at eve in happy simple talk.

The harmless rabbit gambols with its young

   Across the trampled towing-path, where late

A troop of laughing boys in jostling throng

   Cheered with their noisy cries the racing eight;

The gossamer, with ravelled silver threads,

Works at its little loom, and from the dusky red-eaved sheds

Of the lone Farm a flickering light shines out

   Where the swinked shepherd drives his bleating flock

Back to their wattled sheep-cotes, a faint shout

   Comes from some Oxford boat at Sandford lock,

And starts the moor-hen from the sedgy rill,

And the dim lengthening shadows flit like swallows up the hill.

The heron passes homeward to the mere,

   The blue mist creeps among the shivering trees,

Gold world by world the silent stars appear,

And like a blossom blown before the breeze

A white moon drifts across the shimmering sky,

Mute arbitress of all thy sad, thy rapturous threnody.

She does not heed thee, wherefore should she heed,

   She knows Endymion is not far away;

'Tis I, 'tis I, whose soul is as the reed

   Which has no message of its own to play,

So pipes another's bidding, it is I,

Drifting with every wind on the wide sea of misery.

Ah! the brown bird has ceased: one exquisite trill

   About the sombre woodland seems to cling

Dying in music, else the air is still,

   So still that one might hear the bat's small wing

Wander and wheel above the pines, or tell

Each tiny dew-drop dripping from the bluebell's brimming cell.

And far away across the lengthening wold,

   Across the willowy flats and thickets brown,

Magdalen's tall tower tipped with tremulous gold

   Marks the long High Street of the little town,

And warns me to return; I must not wait,

Hark! 't is the curfew booming from the bell at Christ Church gate.

FLOWER OF LOVE

Sweet, I blame you not, for mine the fault

was, had I not been made of common clay

I had climbed the higher heights unclimbed

yet, seen the fuller air, the larger day.

From the wildness of my wasted passion I had

struck a better, clearer song,

Lit some lighter light of freer freedom, battled

with some Hydra-headed wrong.

Had my lips been smitten into music by the

kisses that but made them bleed,

You had walked with Bice and the angels on

that verdant and enamelled mead.

I had trod the road which Dante treading saw

the suns of seven circles shine,

Ay! perchance had seen the heavens opening,

as they opened to the Florentine.

And the mighty nations would have crowned

me, who am crownless now and without name,

And some orient dawn had found me kneeling

on the threshold of the House of Fame.

I had sat within that marble circle where the

oldest bard is as the young,

And the pipe is ever dropping honey, and the

lyre's strings are ever strung.

Keats had lifted up his hymeneal curls from out

the poppy-seeded wine,

With ambrosial mouth had kissed my forehead,

clasped the hand of noble love in mine.

And at springtide, when the apple-blossoms

brush the burnished bosom of the dove,

Two young lovers lying in an orchard would

have read the story of our love;

Would have read the legend of my passion,

known the bitter secret of my heart,

Kissed as we have kissed, but never parted as

we two are fated now to part.

For the crimson flower of our life is eaten by

the cankerworm of truth,

And no hand can gather up the fallen withered

petals of the rose of youth.

Yet I am not sorry that I loved you—ah!

what else had I a boy to do,—

For the hungry teeth of time devour, and the

silent-footed years pursue.

Rudderless, we drift athwart a tempest, and

when once the storm of youth is past,

Without lyre, without lute or chorus, Death

the silent pilot comes at last.

And within the grave there is no pleasure,

for the blindworm battens on the root,

And Desire shudders into ashes, and the tree

of Passion bears no fruit.

Ah! what else had I to do but love you?

God's own mother was less dear to me,

And less dear the Cytheræan rising like an

argent lily from the sea.

I have made my choice, have lived my

poems, and, though youth is gone in wasted days,

I have found the lover's crown of myrtle better

than the poet's crown of bays.

FOOTNOTES

[128] Shelley.

[129] Swinburne.

[136] Rossetti.

[137] Burne-Jones.

SELECTED PROSE OF
OSCAR WILDE

DEDICATION

This anthology is dedicated to Michael Lykiardopulos as a little token of his services to English Literature in the great Russian Empire.

PREFACE

With the possible exceptions of the Greek Anthology, the "Golden Treasury" and those which bear the name of E. V. Lucas, no selections of poetry or prose have ever given complete satisfaction to anyone except the compiler. But critics derive great satisfaction from pointing out errors of omission and inclusion on the part of the anthologist, and all of us have putatively re-arranged and re-edited even the "Golden Treasury" in our leisure moments. In an age when "Art for Art's sake" is an exploded doctrine, anthologies, like everything else, must have a purpose. The purpose or object of the present volume is to afford admirers of Wilde's work the same innocent pleasure obtainable from similar compilations, namely that of reconstructing a selection of their own in their mind's eye—for copyright considerations would interfere with the materialisation of their dream.

A stray observation in an esteemed weekly periodical determined the plan of this anthology and the choice of particular passages. The writer, whose name has escaped me, opined that the reason the works of Pater and Wilde were no longer read was owing to both authors having treated English as a dead language. By a singular coincidence I had purchased simultaneously with the newspaper a shilling copy of Pater's "Renaissance," published by Messrs. Macmillan; and a few days afterwards Messrs. Methuen issued at a shilling the twenty-eighth edition of "De Profundis." Obviously either Messrs. Macmillan and Messrs. Methuen or the authority on dead languages must have been suffering from hallucinations. It occurred to me that a selection of Wilde's prose might at least rehabilitate the notorious reputation for common sense enjoyed by all publishers, who rarely issue shilling editions of deceased authors for mere æsthetic considerations. And I confess to a hope that this volume may reach the eye or ear of those who have not read Wilde's books, or of those, such as Mr. Sydney Grundy, who are irritated by the revival of his plays and the praise accorded to his works throughout the Continent.

Wilde's prose is distinguished by its extraordinary ease and clarity, and by the absence—very singular in his case—of the preciosity which he admired too much in other writers, and advocated with over-emphasis. Perhaps that is why many of his stories and essays and plays are used as English textbooks in Russian and Scandinavian and Hungarian schools. Artifice and affectation, often assumed to be recurrent defects in his writings by those unacquainted with them, are comparatively rare. Wilde once boasted in an interview that only Flaubert, Pater, Keats, and Maeterlinck had influenced him, and then added in a characteristic way: "But I had already gone more than half-way to meet them." Anyone curious as to the origin of Wilde's style and development should consult the learned treatise {1} of Dr. Ernst Bendz, whose comprehensive treatment of the subject renders any elucidation of mine superfluous; while nothing can be added to Mr. Holbrook Jackson's masterly criticism {2} of Wilde and his position in literature.

In making this selection, with the valuable assistance of Mr. Stuart Mason, I have endeavoured to illustrate and to justify the critical appreciations of both Dr. Bendz and Mr. Holbrook Jackson, as well as to afford the general reader a fair idea of Wilde's variety as a prose writer. He is more various than almost any author of the last century, though the act of writing was always a burden to him. Some critic acutely pointed out that poetry and prose were almost side-issues for him. The resulting faults and weakness of what he left are obvious. Except in the plays he has no sustained scheme of thought. Even "De Profundis" is too desultory.

For the purpose of convenient reference I have exercised the prerogative of a literary executor and editor by endowing with special titles some of the pieces quoted in these pages. Though unlike one of Wilde's other friends I cannot claim to have collaborated with him or to have assisted him in any of his plays, I was sometimes permitted, as Wilde acknowledges in different letters, to act in the capacity of godfather by suggesting the actual titles by which some of his books are known to the world. I mention the circumstance only as a precedent for my present temerity. To compensate those who disapprove of my choice, I have included two unpublished letters. The examples of Wilde's epistolary style, published since his death, have been generally associated with disagreeable subjects. Those included here will, I hope, prove a pleasant contrast.

ROBERT ROSS

HOW THEY STRUCK A CONTEMPORARY

There is such a thing as robbing a story of its reality by trying to make it too true, and The Black Arrow is so inartistic as not to contain a single anachronism to boast of, while the transformation of Dr. Jekyll reads dangerously like an experiment out of the Lancet. As for Mr. Rider Haggard, who really has, or had once, the makings of a perfectly magnificent liar, he is now so afraid of being suspected of genius that when he does tell us anything marvellous, he feels bound to invent a personal reminiscence, and to put it into a footnote as a kind of cowardly corroboration. Nor are our other novelists much better. Mr. Henry James writes fiction as if it were a painful duty, and wastes upon mean motives and imperceptible 'points of view' his neat literary style, his felicitous phrases, his swift and caustic satire. Mr. Hall Caine, it is true, aims at the grandiose, but then he writes at the top of his voice. He is so loud that one cannot bear what he says. Mr. James Payn is an adept in the art of concealing what is not worth finding. He hunts down the obvious with the enthusiasm of a short-sighted detective. As one turns over the pages, the suspense of the author becomes almost unbearable. The horses of Mr. William Black's phaeton do not soar towards the sun. They merely frighten the sky at evening into violent chromolithographic effects. On seeing them approach, the peasants take refuge in dialect. Mrs. Oliphant prattles pleasantly about curates, lawn-tennis parties, domesticity, and other wearisome things. Mr. Marion Crawford has immolated himself upon the altar of local colour. He is like the lady in the French comedy who keeps talking about "le beau ciel d'Italie." Besides, he has fallen into the bad habit of uttering moral platitudes. He is always telling us that to be good is to be good, and that to be bad is to be wicked. At times he is almost edifying. Robert Elsmere is of course a masterpiece—a masterpiece of the "genre ennuyeux," the one form of literature that the English people seems thoroughly to enjoy. A thoughtful young friend of ours once told us that it reminded him of the sort of conversation that goes on at a meat tea in the house of a serious Nonconformist family, and we can quite believe it. Indeed it is only in England that such a book could be produced. England is the home of lost ideas. As for that great and daily increasing school of novelists for whom the sun always rises in the East-End, the only thing that can be said about them is that they find life crude, and leave it raw.—*The Decay of Lying.*

THE QUALITY OF GEORGE MEREDITH

Ah! Meredith! Who can define him? His style is chaos illumined by flashes of lightning. As a writer he has mastered everything except language: as a novelist he can do everything, except tell a story: as an artist he is everything except articulate. Somebody in Shakespeare—Touchstone, I think—talks about a man who is always breaking his shins over his own wit, and it seems to me that this might serve as the basis for a criticism of Meredith's method. But whatever he is, he is not a realist. Or rather I would say that he is a child of realism who is not on speaking terms with his father. By deliberate choice he has made himself a romanticist. He has refused to bow the knee to Baal, and after all, even if the man's fine spirit did not revolt against the noisy assertions of realism, his style would be quite sufficient of itself to keep life at a respectful distance. By its means he has planted round his garden a hedge full of thorns, and red with wonderful roses. As for Balzac, he was a most remarkable combination of the artistic temperament with the scientific spirit. The latter he bequeathed to his disciples. The former was entirely his own. The difference between such a book as M. Zola's L'Assommoir and Balzac's Illusions Perdues is the difference between unimaginative realism and imaginative reality. 'All Balzac's characters;' said Baudelaire, 'are gifted with the same ardour of life that animated himself. All his fictions are as deeply coloured as dreams. Each mind is a weapon loaded to the muzzle with will. The very scullions have genius.' A steady course of Balzac reduces our living friends to shadows, and our acquaintances to the shadows of shades. His characters have a kind of fervent fiery-coloured existence. They dominate us, and defy scepticism. One of the greatest tragedies of my life is the death of Lucien de Rubempré. It is a grief from which I have never been able completely to rid myself. It haunts me in my moments of pleasure. I remember it when I laugh. But Balzac is no more a realist than Holbein was. He created life, he did not copy it. I admit, however, that he set far too high a value on modernity of form, and that, consequently, there is no book of his that, as an artistic masterpiece, can rank with *Salammbô or Esmond, or The Cloister and the Hearth, or the Vicomte de Bragelonne.—The Decay of Lying.*

LIFE THE FALLACIOUS MODEL

Art begins with abstract decoration, with purely imaginative and pleasurable work dealing with what is unreal and non-existent. This is the first stage. Then Life becomes fascinated with this new wonder, and asks to be admitted into the charmed circle. Art takes life as part of her rough material, recreates it, and refashions it in fresh forms, is absolutely indifferent to fact, invents, imagines, dreams, and keeps between herself and reality the impenetrable barrier of beautiful style, of decorative or ideal treatment. The third stage is when Life gets the upper hand, and drives Art out into the wilderness. That is the true decadence, and it is from this that we are now suffering.

Take the case of the English drama. At first in the hands of the monks Dramatic Art was abstract, decorative and mythological. Then she enlisted Life in her service, and using some of life's external forms, she created an entirely new race of beings, whose sorrows were more terrible than any sorrow man has ever felt, whose joys were keener than lover's joys, who had the rage of the Titans and the calm of the gods, who had monstrous and marvellous sins, monstrous and marvellous virtues. To them she gave a language different from that of actual use, a language full of resonant music and sweet rhythm, made stately by solemn cadence, or made delicate by fanciful rhyme, jewelled with wonderful words, and enriched with lofty diction. She clothed her children in strange raiment and gave them masks, and at her bidding the antique world rose from its marble tomb. A new Cæsar stalked through the streets of risen Rome, and with purple sail and flute-led oars another Cleopatra passed up the river to Antioch. Old myth and legend and dream took shape and substance. History was entirely re-written, and there was hardly one of the dramatists who did not recognise that the object of Art is not simple truth but complex beauty. In this they were perfectly right. Art itself is really a form of exaggeration; and selection, which is the very spirit of art, is nothing more than an intensified mode of over-emphasis.

But Life soon shattered the perfection of the form. Even in Shakespeare we can see the beginning of the end. It shows itself by the gradual breaking up of the blank-verse in the later plays, by the predominance given to prose and by the over-importance assigned to characterisation. The passages in Shakespeare—and they are many—where the language is uncouth, vulgar exaggerated, fantastic, obscene even, are entirely due to Life calling for an echo of her own voice, and rejecting the intervention of beautiful style through which alone should life be suffered to find expression. Shakespeare is not by any means a flawless artist. He is too fond of going directly to life and borrowing life's natural utterance. He forgets that when Art surrenders her imaginative medium she surrenders everything.—*The Decay of Lying.*

LIFE THE DISCIPLE

We have all seen in our own day in England how a certain curious and fascinating type of beauty, invented and emphasised by two imaginative painters, has so influenced Life that whenever one goes to a private view or to an artistic salon one sees, here the mystic eyes of Rossetti's dream, the long ivory throat, the strange square-cut jaw, the loosened shadowy hair that he so ardently loved, there the sweet maidenhood of 'The Golden Stair,' the blossom-like mouth and weary loveliness of the 'Laus Amoris,' the passion-pale face of Andromeda, the thin hands and lithe beauty of the Vivian in 'Merlin's Dream.' And it has always been so. A great artist invents a type and Life tries to copy it, to reproduce it in a popular form, like an enterprising publisher. Neither Holbein nor Vandyck found in England what they have given us. They brought their types with them, and Life with her keen imitative faculty set herself to supply the master with models. The Greeks, with their quick artistic instinct, understood this, and set in the bride's chamber the statue of Hermes or of Apollo, that she might bear children as lovely as the works of art that she looked at in her rapture or her pain. They knew that Life gains from art not merely spirituality, depth of thought and feeling, soul-turmoil or soul-peace, but that she can form herself on the very lines and colours of art, and can reproduce the dignity of Pheidias as well as the grace of Praxiteles. Hence came their objection to realism. They disliked it on purely social grounds. They felt that it inevitably makes people ugly, and they were perfectly right. We try to improve the conditions of the race by means of good air, free sunlight, wholesome water, and hideous bare buildings for the

124

better housing of the lower orders. But these things merely produce health, they do not produce beauty. For this, Art is required, and the true disciples of the great artist are not his studio-imitators, but those who become like his works of art, be they plastic as in Greek days, or pictorial as in modern times; in a word, Life is Art's best, Art's only pupil.—*The Decay of Lying.*

LIFE THE PLAGIARIST

I once asked a lady, who knew Thackeray intimately, whether he had had any model for Becky Sharp. She told me that Becky was an invention, but that the idea of the character had been partly suggested by a governess who lived in the neighbourhood of Kensington Square, and was the companion of a very selfish and rich old woman. I inquired what became of the governess, and she replied that, oddly enough, some years after the appearance of Vanity Fair, she ran away with the nephew of the lady with whom she was living, and for a short time made a great splash in society, quite in Mrs. Rawdon Crawley's style, and entirely by Mrs. Rawdon Crawley's methods. Ultimately she came to grief, disappeared to the Continent, and used to be occasionally seen at Monte Carlo and other gambling places. The noble gentleman from whom the same great sentimentalist drew Colonel Newcome died, a few months after The Newcomer had reached a fourth edition, with the word 'Adsum' on his lips. Shortly after Mr. Stevenson published his curious psychological story of transformation, a friend of mine, called Mr. Hyde, was in the north of London, and being anxious to get to a railway station, took what he thought would be a short cut, lost his way, and found himself in a network of mean, evil-looking streets. Feeling rather nervous he began to walk extremely fast, when suddenly out of an archway ran a child right between his legs. It fell on the pavement, he tripped over it, and trampled upon it. Being of course very much frightened and a little hurt, it began to scream, and in a few seconds the whole street was full of rough people who came pouring out of the houses like ants. They surrounded him, and asked him his name. He was just about to give it when he suddenly remembered the opening incident in Mr. Stevenson's story. He was so filled with horror at having realised in his own person that terrible and well-written scene, and at having done accidentally, though in fact, what the Mr. Hyde of fiction had done with deliberate intent, that he ran away as hard as he could go. He was, however, very closely followed, and finally he took refuge in a surgery, the door of which happened to be open, where he explained to a young assistant, who happened to be there, exactly what had occurred. The humanitarian crowd were induced to go away on his giving them a small sum of money, and as soon as the coast was clear he left. As he passed out, the name on the brass door-plate of the surgery caught his eye. It was 'Jekyll.' At least it should have been.—*The Decay of Lying.*

THE INDISPENSABLE EAST

What is true about the drama and the novel is no less true about those arts that we call the decorative arts. The whole history of these arts in Europe is the record of the struggle between Orientalism, with its frank rejection of imitation, its love of artistic convention, its dislike to the actual representation of any object in Nature, and our own imitative spirit. Wherever the former has been paramount, as in Byzantium, Sicily and Spain, by actual contact, or in the rest of Europe by the influence of the Crusades, we have had beautiful and imaginative work in which the visible things of life are transmuted into artistic conventions, and the things that Life has not are invented and fashioned for her delight. But wherever we have returned to Life and Nature our work has always become vulgar, common and uninteresting. Modern tapestry, with its aërial effects, its elaborate perspective, its broad expanses of waste sky, its faithful and laborious realism, has no beauty whatsoever. The pictorial glass of Germany is absolutely detestable. We are beginning to weave possible carpets in England, but only because we have returned to the method and spirit of the East. Our rugs and carpets of twenty years ago, with their solemn depressing truths, their inane worship of Nature, their sordid reproductions of visible objects, have become, even to the Philistine, a source of laughter. A cultured Mahomedan once remarked to us, "You Christians are so occupied in misinterpreting the fourth commandment that you have never thought of making an artistic application of the second." He was perfectly right, and the whole truth of the matter is this: The proper school to learn art in is not Life but Art.—*The Decay of Lying.*

THE INFLUENCE OF THE IMPRESSIONISTS ON CLIMATE

Where, if not from the Impressionists, do we get those wonderful brown fogs that come creeping down our streets, blurring the gas-lamps and changing the houses into monstrous shadows? To whom, if not to them and their master, do we owe the lovely silver mists that brood over our river, and turn to faint forms of fading grace curved bridge and swaying barge? The extraordinary change that has taken place in the climate of London during the last ten years is entirely due to a particular school of Art. You smile. Consider the matter from a scientific or a metaphysical point of view, and you will find that I am right. For what is Nature? Nature is no great mother who has borne us. She is our creation. It is in our brain that she quickens to life. Things are because we see them, and what we see, and how we see it, depends on the Arts that have influenced us. To look at a thing is very different from seeing a thing. One does not see anything until one sees its beauty. Then, and then only, does it come into existence. At present, people see fogs, not because there are fogs, but because poets and painters have taught them the mysterious loveliness of such effects. There may have been fogs for centuries in London. I dare say there were. But no one saw them, and so we do not know anything about them. They did not exist till Art had invented them. Now, it must be admitted, fogs are carried to excess. They have become the mere mannerism of a clique, and the exaggerated realism of their method gives dull people bronchitis. Where the cultured catch an effect, the uncultured catch cold. And so, let us be humane, and invite Art to turn her wonderful eyes elsewhere. She has done so already, indeed. That white quivering sunlight that one sees now in France, with its strange blotches of mauve, and its restless violet shadows, is her latest fancy, and, on the whole, Nature reproduces it quite admirably. Where she used to give us Corots and Daubignys, she gives us now exquisite Monets and entrancing Pissaros. Indeed there are moments, rare, it is true, but still to be observed from time to time, when Nature becomes absolutely modern. Of course she is not always to be relied upon. The fact is that she is in this unfortunate position. Art creates an incomparable and unique effect, and, having done so, passes on to other things. Nature, upon the other hand, forgetting that imitation can be made the sincerest form of insult, keeps on repeating this effect until we all become absolutely wearied of it. Nobody of any real culture, for instance, ever talks nowadays about the beauty of a sunset. Sunsets are quite old-fashioned. They belong to the time when Turner was the last note in art. To admire them is a distinct sign of provincialism of temperament. Upon the other hand they go on.—*The Decay of Lying.*

AN EXPOSURE OF NATURALISM

After all, what the imitative arts really give us are merely the various styles of particular artists, or of certain schools of artists. Surely you don't imagine that the people of the Middle Ages bore any resemblance at all to the figures on mediæval stained glass, or in mediæval stone and wood carving, or on mediæval metal-work, or tapestries, or illuminated MSS. They were probably very ordinary-looking people, with nothing grotesque, or remarkable, or fantastic in their appearance. The Middle Ages, as we know them in art, are simply a definite form of style, and there is no reason at all why an artist with this style should not be produced in the nineteenth century. No great artist ever sees things as they really are. If he did, he would cease to be an artist. Take an example from our own day. I know that you are fond of Japanese things. Now, do you really imagine that the Japanese people, as they are presented to us in art, have any existence? If you do, you have never understood Japanese art at all. The Japanese people are the deliberate self-conscious creation of certain individual artists. If you set a picture by Hokusai, or Hokkei, or any of the great native painters, beside a real Japanese gentleman or lady, you will see that there is not the slightest resemblance between them. The actual people who live in Japan are not unlike the general run of English people; that is to say, they are extremely commonplace, and have nothing curious or extraordinary about them. In fact the whole of Japan is a pure invention. There is no such country, there are no such people. One of our most charming painters {3} went recently to the Land of the Chrysanthemum in the foolish hope of seeing the Japanese. All he saw, all he had the chance of painting, were a few lanterns and some fans. He was quite unable to discover the inhabitants, as his delightful exhibition at Messrs. Dowdeswell's Gallery showed only too well. He did not know that the Japanese people are, as I have said, simply a mode of style, an exquisite fancy of art. And so, if you desire to see a Japanese effect, you will not behave like a tourist and go to Tokio. On the contrary, you will stay at home and steep yourself in the work of certain Japanese artists, and then, when you have absorbed the spirit of their style, and caught their imaginative manner of vision, you will go some afternoon and sit in the Park or stroll down Piccadilly, and if you cannot see an absolutely Japanese effect there, you will not see it anywhere. Or, to return again to the past, take as another instance the ancient Greeks. Do you think that Greek art ever tells us what the Greek people were like? Do you believe that the Athenian women were like the stately dignified figures of the Parthenon frieze, or like those marvellous goddesses who sat in the triangular pediments of the same building? If you judge from the art, they certainly were so. But read an authority, like Aristophanes, for instance. You will find that the Athenian ladies laced tightly, wore high-heeled shoes, dyed their hair yellow, painted and rouged their faces, and were exactly like any silly fashionable or fallen creature of our own day. The fact is that we look back on the ages entirely through the medium of art, and art, very fortunately, has never once told us the truth.—*The Decay of Lying.*

THOMAS GRIFFITHS WAINEWRIGHT

He was taken back to Newgate, preparatory to his removal to the colonies. In a fanciful passage in one of his early essays he had fancied himself 'lying in Horsemonger Gaol under sentence of death' for having been unable to resist the temptation of stealing some Marc Antonios from the British Museum in order to complete his collection. The sentence now passed on him was to a man of his culture a form of death. He complained bitterly of it to his friends, and pointed out, with a good deal of reason, some people may fancy, that the money was practically his own, having come to him from his mother, and that the forgery, such as it was, had been committed thirteen years before, which, to use his own phrase, was at least a circonstance attenuante. The permanence of personality is a very subtle metaphysical problem, and certainly the English law solves the question in an extremely rough-and-ready manner. There is, however, something dramatic in the fact that this heavy punishment was inflicted on him for what, if we remember his fatal influence on the prose of modern journalism, was certainly not the worst of all his sins.

While he was in gaol, Dickens, Macready, and Hablot Browne came across him by chance. They had been going over the prisons of London, searching for artistic effects, and in Newgate they suddenly caught sight of Wainewright. He met them with a defiant stare, Forster tells us, but Macready was 'horrified to recognise a man familiarly known to him in former years, and at whose table he had dined.'

Others had more curiosity, and his cell was for some time a kind of fashionable lounge. Many men of letters went down to visit their old literary comrade. But he was no longer the kind light-hearted Janus whom Charles Lamb admired. He seems to have grown quite cynical.

To the agent of an insurance company who was visiting him one afternoon, and thought he would improve the occasion by pointing out that, after all, crime was a bad speculation, he replied: 'Sir, you City men enter on your speculations, and take the chances of them. Some of your speculations succeed, some fail. Mine happen to have failed, yours happen to have succeeded. That is the only difference, sir, between my visitor and me. But, sir, I will tell you one thing in which I have succeeded to the last. I have been determined through life to hold the position of a gentleman. I have always done so. I do so still. It is the custom of this place that each of the inmates of a cell shall take his morning's turn of sweeping it out. I occupy a cell with a bricklayer and a sweep, but they never offer me the broom!' When a friend reproached him with the murder of Helen Abercrombie he shrugged his shoulders and said, 'Yes; it was a dreadful thing to do, but she had very thick ankles.'—*Pen, Pencil and Poison.*

WAINEWRIGHT AT HOBART TOWN

His love of art, however, never deserted him. At Hobart Town he started a studio, and returned to sketching and portrait-painting, and his conversation and manners seem not to have lost their charm. Nor did he give up his habit of poisoning, and there are two cases on record in which he tried to make away with people who had offended him. But his hand seems to have lost its cunning. Both of his attempts were complete failures, and in 1844, being thoroughly dissatisfied with Tasmanian society, he presented a memorial to the governor of the settlement, Sir John Eardley Wilmot, praying for a ticket-of-leave. In it he speaks of himself as being 'tormented by ideas struggling for outward form and realisation, barred up from increase of knowledge, and deprived of the exercise of profitable or even of decorous speech.' His request, however, was refused, and the associate of Coleridge consoled himself by making those marvellous Paradis Artificiels whose secret is only known to the eaters of opium. In 1852 he died of apoplexy, his sole living companion being a cat, for which he had evinced at extraordinary affection.

His crimes seem to have had an important effect upon his art. They gave a strong personality to his style, a quality that his early work certainly lacked. In a note to the Life of Dickens, Forster mentions that in 1847 Lady Blessington received from her brother, Major Power, who held a military appointment at Hobart Town, an oil portrait of a young lady from his clever brush; and it is said that 'he had contrived to put the expression of his own wickedness into the portrait of a nice, kind-hearted girl.' M. Zola, in one of his novels, tells us of a young man who, having committed a murder, takes to art, and paints greenish impressionist portraits of perfectly respectable people, all of which bear a curious resemblance to his victim. The development of Mr. Wainewright's style seems to me far more subtle and suggestive. One can fancy an intense personality being created out of sin.—*Pen, Pencil and Poison.*

CARDINAL NEWMAN AND THE AUTOBIOGRAPHERS

In literature mere egotism is delightful. It is what fascinates us in the letters of personalities so different as Cicero and Balzac, Flaubert and Berlioz, Byron and Madame de Sévigné. Whenever we come across it, and, strangely enough, it is rather rare, we cannot but welcome it, and do not easily forget it. Humanity will always love Rousseau for having confessed his sins, not to a priest, but to the world, and the couchant nymphs that Cellini wrought in bronze for the castle of King Francis, the green and gold Perseus, even, that in the open Loggia at Florence shows the moon the dead terror that once turned life to stone, have not given it more pleasure than has that autobiography in which the supreme scoundrel of the Renaissance relates the story of his splendour and his shame. The opinions, the character, the achievements of the man, matter very little. He may be a sceptic like the gentle Sieur de Montaigne, or a saint like the bitter son of Monica, but when he tells us his own secrets he can always charm our ears to listening and our lips to silence. The mode of thought that Cardinal Newman represented—if that can be called a mode of thought which seeks to solve intellectual problems by a denial of the supremacy of the intellect—may not, cannot, I think, survive. But the world will never weary of watching that troubled soul in its progress from darkness to darkness. The lonely church at Littlemore, where 'the breath of the morning is damp, and worshippers are few,' will always be dear to it, and whenever men see the yellow snapdragon blossoming on the wall of Trinity they will think of that gracious undergraduate who saw in the flower's sure recurrence a prophecy that he would abide for ever with the Benign Mother of his days—a prophecy that Faith, in her wisdom or her folly, suffered not to be fulfilled. Yes; autobiography is irresistible.—*The Critic as Artist.*

ROBERT BROWNING

Taken as a whole the man was great. He did not belong to the Olympians, and had all the incompleteness of the Titan. He did not survey, and it was but rarely that he could sing. His work is marred by struggle, violence and effort, and he passed not from emotion to form, but from thought to chaos. Still, he was great. He has been called a thinker, and was certainly a man who was always thinking, and always thinking aloud; but it was not thought that fascinated him, but rather the processes by which thought moves. It was the machine he loved, not what the machine makes. The method by which the fool arrives at his folly was as dear to him as the ultimate wisdom of the wise. So much, indeed, did the subtle mechanism of mind fascinate him that he despised language, or looked upon it as an incomplete instrument of expression. Rhyme, that exquisite echo which in the Muse's hollow hill creates and answers its own voice; rhyme, which in the hands of the real artist becomes not merely a material element of metrical beauty, but a spiritual element of thought and passion also, waking a new mood, it may be, or stirring a fresh train of ideas, or opening by mere sweetness and suggestion of sound some golden door at which the Imagination itself had knocked in vain; rhyme, which can turn man's utterance to the speech of gods; rhyme, the one chord we have added to the Greek lyre, became in Robert Browning's hands a grotesque, misshapen thing, which at times made him masquerade in poetry as a low comedian, and ride Pegasus too often with his tongue in his cheek. There are moments when he wounds us by monstrous music. Nay, if he can only get his music by breaking the strings of his lute, he breaks them, and they snap in discord, and no Athenian tettix, making melody from tremulous wings, lights on the ivory horn to make the movement perfect, or the interval less harsh. Yet, he was great: and though he turned language into ignoble clay, he made from it men and women that live. He is the most Shakespearian creature since Shakespeare. If Shakespeare could sing with myriad lips, Browning could stammer through a thousand mouths. Even now, as I am speaking, and speaking not against him but for him, there glides through the room the pageant of his persons. There, creeps Fra Lippo Lippi with his cheeks still burning from some girl's hot kiss. There, stands dread Saul with the lordly male-sapphires gleaming in his turban. Mildred Tresham is there, and the Spanish monk, yellow with hatred, and Blougram, and Ben Ezra, and the Bishop of St. Praxed's. The spawn of Setebos gibbers in the corner, and Sebald, hearing Pippa pass by, looks on Ottima's haggard face, and loathes her and his own sin, and himself. Pale as the white satin of his doublet, the melancholy king watches with dreamy treacherous eyes too loyal Strafford pass forth to his doom, and Andrea shudders as he hears the cousins whistle in the garden, and bids his perfect wife go down. Yes, Browning was great. And as what will he be remembered? As a poet? Ah, not as a poet! He will be remembered as a writer of fiction, as the most supreme writer of fiction, it may be, that we have ever had. His sense of dramatic situation was unrivalled, and, if he could not answer his own problems, he could at least put problems forth, and what more should an artist do? Considered from the point of view of a creator of character he ranks next to him who made Hamlet. Had he been articulate, he might have sat beside him. The only man who can touch the hem of his garment is George Meredith. Meredith is a prose Browning, and so is Browning. He used poetry as a medium for writing in prose.—*The Critic as Artist.*

THE TWO SUPREME AND HIGHEST ARTS

Life and Literature, life and the perfect expression of life. The principles of the former, as laid down by the Greeks, we may not realise in an age so marred by false ideals as our own. The principles of the latter, as they laid them down, are, in many cases, so subtle that we can hardly understand them. Recognising that the most perfect art is that which most fully mirrors man in all his infinite variety, they elaborated the criticism of language, considered in the light of the mere material of that art, to a point to which we, with our accentual system of reasonable or emotional emphasis, can barely if at all attain; studying, for instance, the metrical movements of a prose as scientifically as a modern musician studies harmony and counterpoint, and, I need hardly say, with much keener æsthetic instinct. In this they were right, as they were right in all things. Since the introduction of printing, and the fatal development of the habit of reading amongst the middle and lower classes of this country, there has been a tendency in literature to appeal more and more to the eye, and less and less to the ear which is really the sense which, from the standpoint of pure art, it should seek to please, and by whose canons of pleasure it should abide always. Even the work of Mr. Pater, who is, on the whole, the most perfect master of English prose now creating amongst us, is often far more like a piece of mosaic than a passage in music, and seems, here and there, to lack the true rhythmical life of words and the fine freedom and richness of effect that such rhythmical life produces. We, in fact, have made writing a definite mode of composition, and have treated it as a form of elaborate design. The Greeks, upon the other hand, regarded writing simply as a method of chronicling. Their test was always the spoken word in its musical and metrical relations. The voice was the medium, and the ear the critic. I have sometimes thought that the story of Homer's blindness might be really an artistic myth, created in critical days, and serving to remind us, not merely that the great poet is always a seer, seeing less with the eyes of the body than he does with the eyes of the soul, but that he is a true singer also, building his song out of music, repeating each line over and over again to himself till he has caught the secret of its melody, chaunting in darkness the words that are winged with light. Certainly, whether this be so or not, it was to his blindness, as an occasion, if not as a cause, that England's great poet owed much of the majestic movement and sonorous splendour of his later verse. When Milton could no longer write he began to sing.—*The Critic as Artist.*

THE SECRETS OF IMMORTALITY

On the mouldering citadel of Troy lies the lizard like a thing of green bronze. The owl has built her nest in the palace of Priam. Over the empty plain wander shepherd and goatherd with their flocks, and where, on the wine-surfaced, oily sea, οινοψ ποντος, as Homer calls it, copper-prowed and streaked with vermilion, the great galleys of the Danaoi came in their gleaming crescent, the lonely tunny-fisher sits in his little boat and watches the bobbing corks of his net. Yet, every morning the doors of the city are thrown open, and on foot, or in horse-drawn chariot, the warriors go forth to battle, and mock their enemies from behind their iron masks. All day long the fight rages, and when night comes the torches gleam by the tents, and the cresset burns in the hall. Those who live in marble or on painted panel, know of life but a single exquisite instant, eternal indeed in its beauty, but limited to one note of passion or one mood of calm. Those whom the poet makes live have their myriad emotions of joy and terror, of courage and despair, of pleasure and of suffering. The seasons come and go in glad or saddening pageant, and with winged or leaden feet the years pass by before them. They have their youth and their manhood, they are children, and they grow old. It is always dawn for St. Helena, as Veronese saw her at the window. Through the still morning air the angels bring her the symbol of God's pain. The cool breezes of the morning lift the gilt threads from her brow. On that little hill by the city of Florence, where the lovers of Giorgione are lying, it is always the solstice of noon, of noon made so languorous by summer suns that hardly can the slim naked girl dip into the marble tank the round bubble of clear glass, and the long fingers of the lute-player rest idly upon the chords. It is twilight always for the dancing nymphs whom Corot set free among the silver poplars of France. In eternal twilight they move, those frail diaphanous figures, whose tremulous white feet seem not to touch the dew-drenched grass they tread on. But those who walk in epos, drama, or romance, see through the labouring months the young moons wax and wane, and watch the night from evening unto morning star, and from sunrise unto sunsetting can note the shifting day with all its gold and shadow. For them, as for us, the flowers bloom and wither, and the Earth, that Green-tressed Goddess as Coleridge calls her, alters her raiment for their pleasure. The statue is concentrated to one moment of perfection. The image stained upon the canvas possesses no spiritual element of growth or change. If they know nothing of death, it is because they know little of life, for the secrets of life and death belong to those, and those only, whom the sequence of time affects, and who possess not merely the present but the future, and can rise or fall from a past of glory or of shame. Movement, that problem of the visible arts, can be truly realised by Literature alone. It is Literature that shows us the body in its swiftness and the soul in its unrest.—*The Critic as Artist.*

THE CRITIC AND HIS MATERIAL

Who cares whether Mr. Ruskin's views on Turner are sound or not? What does it matter? That mighty and majestic prose of his, so fervid and so fiery-coloured in its noble eloquence, so rich in its elaborate symphonic music, so sure and certain, at its best, in subtle choice of word and epithet is at least as great a work of art as any of those wonderful sunsets that bleach or rot on their corrupted canvases in England's Gallery; greater indeed one is apt to think at times, not merely because its equal beauty is more enduring, but on account of the fuller variety of its appeal, soul speaking to soul in those long-cadenced lines, not through form and colour alone, though through these, indeed, completely and without loss, but with intellectual and emotional utterance, with lofty passion and with loftier thought, with imaginative insight, and with poetic aim; greater, I always think, even as Literature is the greater art. Who, again, cares whether Mr. Pater has put into the portrait of Monna Lisa something that Lionardo never dreamed of? The painter may have been merely the slave of an archaic smile, as some have fancied, but whenever I pass into the cool galleries of the Palace of the Louvre and stand before that strange figure 'set in its marble chair in that cirque of fantastic rocks, as in some faint light under sea,' I murmur to myself, 'She is older than the rocks among which she sits; like the vampire, she has been dead many times, and learned the secrets of the grave; and has been a diver in deep seas, and keeps their fallen day about her: and trafficked for strange webs with Eastern merchants; and, as Leda, was the mother of Helen of Troy, and, as St. Anne, the mother of Mary; and all this has been to her but as the sound of lyres and flutes, and lives only in the delicacy with which it has moulded the changing lineaments, and tinged the eyelids and the hands.' And I say to my friend, 'The presence that thus so strangely rose beside the waters is expressive of what in the ways of a thousand years man had come to desire'; and he answers me, 'Hers is the head upon which all "the ends of the world are come," and the eyelids are a little weary.'

And so the picture becomes more wonderful to us than it really is, and reveals to us a secret of which, in truth, it knows nothing, and the music of the mystical prose is as sweet in our ears as was that flute-player's music that lent to the lips of La Gioconda those subtle and poisonous curves. Do you ask me what Lionardo would have said had any one told him of this picture that 'all the thoughts and experience of the world had etched and moulded therein that which they had of power to refine and make expressive the outward form, the animalism of Greece, the lust of Rome, the reverie of the Middle Age with its spiritual ambition and imaginative loves, the return of the Pagan world, the sins of the Borgias?' He would probably have answered that he had contemplated none of these things, but had concerned himself simply with certain arrangements of lines and masses, and with new and curious colour-harmonies of blue and green. And it is for this very reason that the criticism which I have quoted is criticism of the highest kind. It treats the work of art simply as a starting-point for a new creation. It does not confine itself—let us at least suppose so for the moment—to discovering the real intention of the artist and accepting that as final. And in this it is right, for the meaning of any beautiful created thing is, at least, as much in the soul of him who looks at it, as it was in his soul who wrought it. Nay, it is rather the beholder who lends to the beautiful thing its myriad meanings, and makes it marvellous for us, and sets it in some new relation to the age, so that it becomes a vital portion of our lives, and a symbol of what we pray for, or perhaps of what, having prayed for, we fear that we may receive.—*The Critic as Artist.*

DANTE THE LIVING GUIDE

There is no mood or passion that Art cannot give us, and those of us who have discovered her secret can settle beforehand what our experiences are going to be. We can choose our day and select our hour. We can say to ourselves, 'To-morrow, at dawn, we shall walk with grave Virgil through the valley of the shadow of death,' and lo! the dawn finds us in the obscure wood, and the Mantuan stands by our side. We pass through the gate of the legend fatal to hope, and with pity or with joy behold the horror of another world. The hypocrites go by, with their painted faces and their cowls of gilded lead. Out of the ceaseless winds that drive them, the carnal look at us, and we watch the heretic rending his flesh, and the glutton lashed by the rain. We break the withered branches from the tree in the grove of the Harpies, and each dull-hued poisonous twig bleeds with red blood before us, and cries aloud with bitter cries. Out of a horn of fire Odysseus speaks to us, and when from his sepulchre of flame the great Ghibelline rises, the pride that triumphs over the torture of that bed becomes ours for a moment. Through the dim purple air fly those who have stained the world with the beauty of their sin, and in the pit of loathsome disease, dropsy-stricken and swollen of body into the semblance of a monstrous lute, lies Adamo di Brescia, the coiner of false coin. He bids us listen to his misery; we stop, and with dry and gaping lips he tells us how he dreams day and night of the brooks of clear water that in cool dewy channels gush down the green Casentine hills. Sinon, the false Greek of Troy, mocks at him. He smites him in the face, and they wrangle. We are fascinated by their shame, and loiter, till Virgil chides us and leads us away to that city turreted by giants where great Nimrod blows his horn. Terrible things are in store for us, and we go to meet them in Dante's raiment and with Dante's heart. We traverse the marshes of the Styx, and Argenti swims to the boat through the slimy waves. He calls to us, and we reject him. When we hear the voice of his agony we are glad, and Virgil praises us for the bitterness of our scorn. We tread upon the cold crystal of Cocytus, in which traitors stick like straws in glass. Our foot strikes against the head of Bocca. He will not tell us his name, and we tear the hair in handfuls from the screaming skull. Alberigo prays us to break the ice upon his face that he may weep a little. We pledge our word to him, and when he has uttered his dolorous tale we deny the word that we have spoken, and pass from him; such cruelty being courtesy indeed, for who more base than he who has mercy for the condemned of God? In the jaws of Lucifer we see the man who sold Christ, and in the jaws of Lucifer the men who slew Cæsar. We tremble, and come forth to re-behold the stars.—*The Critic as Artist.*

THE LIMITATIONS OF GENIUS

The appeal of all Art is simply to the artistic temperament. Art does not address herself to the specialist. Her claim is that she is universal, and that in all her manifestations she is one. Indeed, so far from its being true that the artist is the best judge of art, a really great artist can never judge of other people's work at all, and can hardly, in fact, judge of his own. That very concentration of vision that makes a man an artist, limits by its sheer intensity his faculty of fine appreciation. The energy of creation hurries him blindly on to his own goal. The wheels of his chariot raise the dust as a cloud around him. The gods are hidden from each other. They can recognise their worshippers. That is all . . . Wordsworth saw in Endymion merely a pretty piece of Paganism, and Shelley, with his dislike of actuality, was deaf to Wordsworth's message, being repelled by its form, and Byron, that great passionate human incomplete creature, could appreciate neither the poet of the cloud nor the poet of the lake, and the wonder of Keats was hidden from him. The realism of Euripides was hateful to Sophokles. Those droppings of warm tears had no music for him. Milton, with his sense of the grand style, could not understand the method of Shakespeare, any more than could Sir Joshua the method of Gainsborough. Bad artists always admire each other's work. They call it being large-minded and free from prejudice. But a truly great artist cannot conceive of life being shown, or beauty fashioned, under any conditions other than those that he has selected. Creation employs all its critical faculty within its own sphere. It may not use it in the sphere that belongs to others. It is exactly because a man cannot do a thing that he is the proper judge of it.—*The Critic as Artist.*

WANTED A NEW BACKGROUND

He who would stir us now by fiction must either give us an entirely new background, or reveal to us the soul of man in its innermost workings. The first is for the moment being done for us by Mr. Rudyard Kipling. As one turns over the pages of his Plain Tales from the Hills, one feels as if one were seated under a palm-tree reading life by superb flashes of vulgarity. The bright colours of the bazaars dazzle one's eyes. The jaded, second-rate Anglo-Indians are in exquisite incongruity with their surroundings. The mere lack of style in the story-teller gives an odd journalistic realism to what he tells us. From the point of view of literature Mr. Kipling is a genius who drops his aspirates. From the point of view of life, he is a reporter who knows vulgarity better than any one has ever known it. Dickens knew its clothes and its comedy. Mr. Kipling knows its essence and its seriousness. He is our first authority on the second-rate, and has seen marvellous things through keyholes, and his backgrounds are real works of art. As for the second condition, we have had Browning, and Meredith is with us. But there is still much to be done in the sphere of introspection. People sometimes say that fiction is getting too morbid. As far as psychology is concerned, it has never been morbid enough. We have merely touched the surface of the soul, that is all. In one single ivory cell of the brain there are stored away things more marvellous and more terrible than even they have dreamed of, who, like the author of Le Rouge et le Noir, have sought to track the soul into its most secret places, and to make life confess its dearest sins. Still, there is a limit even to the number of untried backgrounds, and it is possible that a further development of the habit of introspection may prove fatal to that creative faculty to which it seeks to supply fresh material. I myself am inclined to think that creation is doomed. It springs from too primitive, too natural an impulse. However this may be, it is certain that the subject-matter at the disposal of creation is always diminishing, while the subject-matter of criticism increases daily. There are always new attitudes for the mind, and new points of view. The duty of imposing form upon chaos does not grow less as the world advances. There was never a time when Criticism was more needed than it is now. It is only by its means that Humanity can become conscious of the point at which it has arrived.—*The Critic as Artist.*

WITHOUT FRONTIERS

Goethe—you will not misunderstand what I say—was a German of the Germans. He loved his country—no man more so. Its people were dear to him; and he led them. Yet, when the iron hoof of Napoleon trampled upon vineyard and cornfield, his lips were silent. 'How can one write songs of hatred without hating?' he said to Eckermann, 'and how could I, to whom culture and barbarism are alone of importance, hate a nation which is among the most cultivated of the earth and to which I owe so great a part of my own cultivation?' This note, sounded in the modern world by Goethe first, will become, I think, the starting point for the cosmopolitanism of the future. Criticism will annihilate race-prejudices, by insisting upon the unity of the human mind in the variety of its forms. If we are tempted to make war upon another nation, we shall remember that we are seeking to destroy an element of our own culture, and possibly its most important element. As long as war is regarded as wicked, it will always have its fascination. When it is looked upon as vulgar, it will cease to be popular. The change will of course be slow, and people will not be conscious of it. They will not say 'We will not war

140

against France because her prose is perfect,' but because the prose of France is perfect, they will not hate the land. Intellectual criticism will bind Europe together in bonds far closer than those that can be forged by shopman or sentimentalist. It will give us the peace that springs from understanding.— *The Critic as Artist.*

THE POETRY OF ARCHÆOLOGY

Infessura tells us that in 1485 some workmen digging on the Appian Way came across an old Roman sarcophagus inscribed with the name 'Julia, daughter of Claudius.' On opening the coffer they found within its marble womb the body of a beautiful girl of about fifteen years of age, preserved by the embalmer's skill from corruption and the decay of time. Her eyes were half open, her hair rippled round her in crisp curling gold, and from her lips and cheek the bloom of maidenhood had not yet departed. Borne back to the Capitol, she became at once the centre of a new cult, and from all parts of the city crowded pilgrims to worship at the wonderful shrine, till the Pope, fearing lest those who had found the secret of beauty in a Pagan tomb might forget what secrets Judæa's rough and rock-hewn sepulchre contained, had the body conveyed away by night, and in secret buried. Legend though it may be, yet the story is none the less valuable as showing us the attitude of the Renaissance towards the antique world. Archæology to them was not a mere science for the antiquarian; it was a means by which they could touch the dry dust of antiquity into the very breath and beauty of life, and fill with the new wine of romanticism forms that else had been old and outworn. From the pulpit of Niccola Pisano down to Mantegna's 'Triumph of Cæsar,' and the service Cellini designed for King Francis, the influence of this spirit can be traced; nor was it confined merely to the immobile arts—the arts of arrested movement—but its influence was to be seen also in the great Græco-Roman masques which were the constant amusement of the gay courts of the time, and in the public pomps and processions with which the citizens of big commercial towns were wont to greet the princes that chanced to visit them; pageants, by the way, which were considered so important that large prints were made of them and published—a fact which is a proof of the general interest at the time in matters of such kind.—*The Truth of Masks.*

THE ART OF ARCHÆOLOGY

Indeed archæology is only really delightful when transfused into some form of art. I have no desire to underrate the services of laborious scholars, but I feel that the use Keats made of Lemprière's Dictionary is of far more value to us than Professor Max Müller's treatment of the same mythology as a disease of language. Better Endymion than any theory, however sound, or, as in the present instance, unsound, of an epidemic among adjectives! And who does not feel that the chief glory of Piranesi's book on Vases is that it gave Keats the suggestion for his 'Ode on a Grecian Urn'? Art, and art only, can make archæology beautiful; and the theatric art can use it most directly and most vividly, for it can combine in one exquisite presentation the illusion of actual life with the wonder of the unreal world. But the sixteenth century was not merely the age of Vitruvius; it was the age of Vecellio also. Every nation seems suddenly to have become interested in the dress of its neighbours. Europe began to investigate its own clothes, and the amount of books published on national costumes is quite extraordinary. At the beginning of the century the Nuremberg Chronicle, with its two thousand illustrations, reached its fifth edition, and before the century was over seventeen editions were published of Munster's Cosmography. Besides these two books there were also the works of Michael Colyns, of Hans Weigel, of Amman, and of Vecellio himself, all of them well illustrated, some of the drawings in Vecellio being probably from the hand of Titian.

Nor was it merely from books and treatises that they acquired their knowledge. The development of the habit of foreign travel, the increased commercial intercourse between countries, and the frequency of diplomatic missions, gave every nation many opportunities of studying the various forms of contemporary dress. After the departure from England, for instance, of the ambassadors from the Czar, the Sultan and the Prince of Morocco, Henry the Eighth and his friends gave several masques in the strange attire of their visitors. Later on London saw, perhaps too often, the sombre splendour of the Spanish Court, and to Elizabeth came envoys from all lands, whose dress Shakespeare tells us, had an important influence on English costume.—The *Truth of Masks.*

HEROD SUPPLIANT

Non, non, vous ne voulez pas cela. Vous me dites cela seulement pour me faire de la peine, parce que je vous ai regardée pendant toute la soirée. Eh! bien, oui. Je vous ai regardée pendant toute la soirée. Votre beauté m'a troublé. Votre beauté m'a terriblement troublé, et je vous ai trop regardée. Mais je ne le ferai plus. Il ne faut regarder ni les choses ni les personnes. Il ne faut regarder que dans les miroirs. Car les miroirs ne nous montrent que des masques . . . Oh! Oh! du vin! j'ai soif . . . Salomé, Salomé, soyons amis. Enfin, voyez . . . Qu'est-ce que je voulais dire? Qu'est-ce que c'était? Ah! je m'en souviens! . . . Salomé! Non, venez plus près de moi. J'ai peur que vous ne m'entendiez pas . . . Salomé, vous connaissez mes paons blancs, mes beaux paons blancs, qui se promènent dans le jardin entre les myrtes et les grands cyprès. Leurs becs sont dorés, et les grains qu'ils mangent sont dorés aussi, et leurs pieds sont teints de pourpre. La pluie vient quand ils crient, et quand ils se pavanent la lune se montre au ciel. Ils vont deux à deux entre les cyprès et les myrtes noirs et chacun a son esclave pour le soigner. Quelquefois ils volent à travers les arbres, et quelquefois ils couchent sur le gazon et autour de l'étang. Il n'y a pas dans le monde d'oiseaux si merveilleux. Il n'y a aucun roi du monde qui possède des oiseaux aussi merveilleux. Je suis sûr que même César ne possède pas d'oiseaux aussi beaux. Eh bien! je vous donnerai cinquante de mes paons. Ils vous suivront partout, et au milieu d'eux vous serez comme la lune dans un grand nuage blanc . . . Je vous les donnerai tous. Je n'en ai que cent, et il n'y a aucun roi du monde qui possède des paons comme les miens, mais je vous les donnerai tous. Seulement, il faut me délier de ma parole et ne pas me demander ce que vous m'avez demandé.—*Salomé.*

THE TETRARCH'S REMORSE

Salomé, pensez à ce que vous faites. Cet homme vient peut-être de Dieu. Je suis sûr qu'il vient de Dieu. C'est un saint homme. Le doigt de Dieu l'a touché. Dieu a mis dans sa bouche des mots terribles. Dans le palais, comme dans le désert, Dieu est toujours avec lui . . . Au moins, c'est possible. On ne sait pas, mais il est possible que Dieu soit pour lui et avec lui. Aussi peut-être que s'il mourrait, il m'arriverait un malheur. Enfin, il a dit que le jour où il mourrait il arriverait un malheur à quelqu'un. Ce ne peut être qu'à moi. Souvenez-vous, j'ai glissé dans le sang quand je suis entré ici. Aussi j'a entendu un battement d'ailes dans l'air, un battement d'ailes gigantesques Ce sont de très mauvais présages. Et il y en avait d'autres. Je suis sûr qu'il y er avait d'autres, quoique je ne les aie pas vus. Eh bien! Salomé, vous ne voulez pas qu'un malheur m'arrive? Vous ne voulez pas cela.—*Salomé.*

THE TETRARCH'S TREASURE

Moi, je suis très calme. Je suis tout à fait calme. Écoutez. J'ai des bijoux cachés ici que même votre mère n'a jamais vus, des bijoux tout à fait extraordinaires. J'ai un collier de perles à quatre rangs. On dirait des lunes enchaînées de rayons d'argent. On dirait cinquante lunes captives dans un filet d'or. Une reine l'a porté sur l'ivoire de ses seins. Toi, quand tu le porteras, tu seras aussi belle qu'une reine. J'ai des améthystes de deux espèces Une qui est noire comme le vin. L'autre qui est rouge comme du vin qu'on a coloré avec de l'eau. J'ai des topazes jaunes comme les yeux des tigres, et des topazes roses comme les yeux des pigeons, et des topazes vertes comme les yeux des chats. J'ai des opales qui brûlent toujours avec une flamme qui est très froide, des opales qui attristent les esprits et ont peur des ténèbres. J'ai des onyx semblables aux prunelles d'une morte. J'ai des sélénites qui changent quand la lune change et deviennent pâles quand elles voient le soleil. J'ai des saphirs grands comme des oeufs et bleus comme des fleurs bleues. La mer erre dedans, et la lune ne vient jamais troubler le bleu de ses flots. J'ai des chrysolithes et des béryls, j'ai des chrysoprases et des rubis, j'ai des sardonyx et des hyacinthes, et des calcédoines et je vous les donnerai tous, mais tous, et j'ajouterai d'autres choses. Le roi des Indes vient justement de m'envoyer quatre éventails faits de plumes de perroquets, et le roi de Numidie une robe faite de plumes d'autruche. J'ai un cristal qu'il n'est pas permis aux femmes de voir et que même les jeunes hommes ne doivent regarder qu'après avoir été flagellés de verges. Dans un coffret de nacre j'ai trois turquoises merveilleuses. Quand on les porte sur le front on peut imaginer des choses qui n'existent pas, et quand on les porte dans la main on peut rendre les femmes stériles. Ce sont des trésors de grande valeur. Ce sont des trésors sans prix. Et ce n'est pas tout. Dans un coffret d'ébène j'ai deux coupes d'ambre qui ressemblent à des pommes d'or. Si un ennemi verse du poison dans ces coupes elles deviennent comme des pommes d'argent. Dans un coffret incrusté d'ambre j'ai des sandales incrustées de verre. J'ai des manteaux qui viennent du pays des Sères et des bracelets garnis d'escarboucles et de jade qui viennent de la ville d'Euphrate. . . Enfin, que veux-tu, Salomé? Dis-moi ce que tu désires et je te le donnerai. Je te donnerai tout ce que tu demanderas, sauf une chose. Je te donnerai tout ce que je possède, sauf une vie. Je te donnerai le manteau du grand prêtre. Je te donnerai le voile du sanctuaire.—*Salomé.*

SALOMÉ ANTICIPATES DR. STRAUSS

Ah! tu n'as pas voulu me laisser baiser ta bouche, Iokanaan. Eh bien! je la baiserai maintenant. Je la mordrai avec mes dents comme on mord un fruit mûr. Oui, je baiserai ta bouche, Iokanaan. Je te l'ai dit, n'est-ce pas? je te l'ai dit. Eh bien! je la baiserai maintenant . . . Mais pourquoi ne me regardes-tu pas, Iokanaan? Tes yeux qui étaient si terribles, qui étaient si pleins de colère et de mépris, ils sont fermés maintenant. Pourquoi sont-ils fermés? Ouvre tes yeux! Soulève tes paupières, Iokanaan. Pourquoi ne me regardes-tu pas? As-tu peur de moi, Iokanaan, que tu ne veux pas me regarder? . . . Et ta langue qui était comme un serpent rouge dardant des poisons, elle ne remue plus, elle ne dit rien maintenant, Iokanaan, cette vipère rouge qui a vomi son venin sur moi. C'est étrange, n'est-ce pas? Comment se fait-il que la vipère rouge ne remue plus? . . . Tu n'as pas voulu de moi, Iokanaan. Tu m'as rejetée. Tu m'as dit des choses infâmes. Tu m'as traitée comme une courtisane, comme une prostituée, moi, Salomé, fille d'Hérodias, Princesse de Judée! Eh bien, Iokanaan, moi je vis encore, mais toi tu es mort et ta tête m'appartient. Je puis en faire ce que je veux. Je puis la jeter aux chiens et aux oiseaux de l'air. Ce que laisseront les chiens, les oiseaux de l'air le mangeront . . . Ah! Iokanaan, Iokanaan, tu as été le seul homme que j'ai aimé. Tous les autres hommes m'inspirent du dégoût. Mais, toi, tu étais beau. Ton corps était une colonne d'ivoire sur un socle d'argent. C'était un jardin plein de colombes et de lis d'argent. C'était une tour d'argent ornée de boucliers d'ivoire. Il n'y avait rien au monde d'aussi blanc que ton corps. Il n'y avait rien au monde d'aussi noir que tes cheveux. Dans le monde tout entier il n'y avait rien d'aussi rouge que ta bouche. Ta voix était un encensoir qui répandait d'étranges parfums, et quand je te regardais j'entendais une musique étrange! Ah! pourquoi ne m'as-tu pas regardée, Iokanaan? Derrière tes mains et tes blasphèmes tu as caché ton visage. Tu as mis sur tes yeux le bandeau de celui qui veut voir son

145

Dieu. Eh bien, tu l'as vu, ton Dieu, Iokanaan, mais moi, moi . . . tu ne m'as jamais vue. Si tu m'avais vue, tu m'aurais aimée. Moi, je t'ai vu, Iokanaan, et je t'ai aimé. Oh! comme je t'ai aimé. Je t'aime encore, Iokanaan. Je n'aime que toi . . . J'ai soif de ta beauté. J'ai faim de ton corps. Et ni le vin, ni les fruits ne peuvent apaiser mon désir. Que ferai-je, Iokanaan, maintenant? Ni les fleuves ni les grandes eaux, ne pourraient éteindre ma passion. J'étais une Princesse, tu m'as dédaignée. J'étais une vierge, tu m'as déflorée. J'étais chaste, tu as rempli mes veines de feu . . . Ah! Ah! pourquoi ne m'as-tu pas regardée, Iokanaan? Si tu m'avais regardée tu m'aurais aimée. Je sais bien que tu m'aurais aimée, et le mystère de l'amour est plus grand que le mystére de la mort. Il ne faut regarder que l'amour.—*Salomé*.

THE YOUNG KING

All rare and costly materials had certainly a great fascination for him, and in his eagerness to procure them he had sent away many merchants, some to traffic for amber with the rough fisher-folk of the north seas, some to Egypt to look for that curious green turquoise which is found only in the tombs of kings, and is said to possess magical properties, some to Persia for silken carpets and painted pottery, and others to India to buy gauze and stained ivory, moonstones and bracelets of jade, sandal-wood and blue enamel and shawls of fine wool.

But what had occupied him most was the robe he was to wear at his coronation, the robe of tissued gold, and the ruby-studded crown, and the sceptre with its rows and rings of pearls. Indeed, it was of this that he was thinking to-night, as he lay back on his luxurious couch, watching the great pinewood log that was burning itself out on the open hearth. The designs, which were from the hands of the most famous artists of the time, had been submitted to him many months before, and he had given orders that the artificers were to toil night and day to carry them out, and that the whole world was to be searched for jewels that would be worthy of their work. He saw himself in fancy standing at the high altar of the cathedral in the fair raiment of a King, and a smile played and lingered about his boyish lips, and lit up with a bright lustre his dark woodland eyes.

After some time he rose from his seat, and leaning against the carved

146

penthouse of the chimney, looked round at the dimly-lit room. The walls were hung with rich tapestries representing the Triumph of Beauty. A large press, inlaid with agate and lapis-lazuli, filled one corner, and facing the window stood a curiously wrought cabinet with lacquer panels of powdered and mosaiced gold, on which were placed some delicate goblets of Venetian glass, and a cup of dark-veined onyx. Pale poppies were broidered on the silk coverlet of the bed, as though they had fallen from the tired hands of sleep, and tall reeds of fluted ivory bare up the velvet canopy, from which great tufts of ostrich plumes sprang, like white foam, to the pallid silver of the fretted ceiling. A laughing Narcissus in green bronze held a polished mirror above its head. On the table stood a flat bowl of amethyst.

Outside he could see the huge dome of the cathedral, looming like a bubble over the shadowy houses, and the weary sentinels pacing up and down on the misty terrace by the river. Far away, in an orchard, a nightingale was singing. A faint perfume of jasmine came through the open window. He brushed his brown curls back from his forehead, and taking up a lute, let his fingers stray across the cords. His heavy eyelids drooped, and a strange languor came over him. Never before had he felt so keenly, or with such exquisite joy, the magic and the mystery of beautiful things.

When midnight sounded from the clock-tower he touched a bell, and his pages entered and disrobed him with much ceremony, pouring rose-water over his hands, and strewing flowers on his pillow. A few moments after that they had left the room, he fell asleep.—*The Young King.*

A CORONATION

And when the Bishop had heard them he knit his brows, and said, 'My son, I am an old man, and in the winter of my days, and I know that many evil things are done in the wide world. The fierce robbers come down from the mountains, and carry off the little children, and sell them to the Moors. The lions lie in wait for the caravans, and leap upon the camels. The wild boar roots up the corn in the valley, and the foxes gnaw the vines upon the hill. The pirates lay waste the sea-coast and burn the ships of the fishermen, and take their nets from them. In the salt-marshes live the lepers; they have houses of wattled reeds, and none may come nigh them. The beggars wander through the cities, and eat their food with the dogs. Canst thou make these things not to be? Wilt thou take the leper for thy bedfellow, and set the beggar at thy board? Shall the lion do thy bidding, and the wild boar obey thee? Is not He who made misery wiser than thou art? Wherefore I praise thee not for this that thou hast done, but I bid thee ride back to the Palace and make thy face glad, and put on the raiment that beseemeth a king, and with the crown of gold I will crown thee, and the sceptre of pearl will I place in thy hand. And as for thy dreams, think no more of them. The burden of this world is too great for one man to bear, and the world's sorrow too heavy for one heart to suffer.'

'Sayest thou that in this house?' said the young King, and he strode past the Bishop, and climbed up the steps of the altar, and stood before the image of Christ.

He stood before the image of Christ, and on his right hand and on his left were the marvellous vessels of gold, the chalice with the yellow wine, and the vial with the holy oil. He knelt before the image of Christ, and the great candles burned brightly by the jewelled shrine, and the smoke of the incense curled in thin blue wreaths through the dome. He bowed his head in prayer, and the priests in their stiff copes crept away from the altar.

And suddenly a wild tumult came from the street outside, and in entered the nobles with drawn swords and nodding plumes, and shields of polished steel. 'Where is this dreamer of dreams?' they cried. 'Where is this King who is apparelled like a beggar—this boy who brings shame upon our state? Surely we will slay him, for he is unworthy to rule over us.'

And the young King bowed his head again, and prayed, and when he had finished his prayer he rose up, and turning round he looked at them sadly.

And lo! through the painted windows came the sunlight streaming upon him, and the sun-beams wove round him a tissued robe that was fairer than the robe that had been fashioned for his pleasure. The dead staff blossomed, and bare lilies that were whiter than pearls. The dry thorn blossomed, and bare roses that were redder than rubies. Whiter than fine pearls were the lilies, and their stems were of bright silver. Redder than male rubies were the

148

roses, and their leaves were of beaten gold.

He stood there in the raiment of a king, and the gates of the jewelled shrine flew open, and from the crystal of the many-rayed monstrance shone a marvellous and mystical light. He stood there in a king's raiment, and the Glory of God filled the place, and the saints in their carven niches seemed to move. In the fair raiment of a king he stood before them, and the organ pealed out its music, and the trumpeters blew upon their trumpets, and the singing boys sang.

And the people fell upon their knees in awe, and the nobles sheathed their swords and did homage, and the Bishop's face grew pale, and his hands trembled. 'A greater than I hath crowned thee,' he cried, and he knelt before him.

And the young King came down from the high altar, and passed home through the midst of the people. But no man dared look upon his face, for it was like the face of an angel.—*The Young King.*

THE KING OF SPAIN

From a window in the palace the sad melancholy King watched them. Behind him stood his brother, Don Pedro of Aragon, whom he hated, and his confessor, the Grand Inquisitor of Granada, sat by his side. Sadder even than usual was the King, for as he looked at the Infanta bowing with childish gravity to the assembling counters, or laughing behind her fan at the grim Duchess of Albuquerque who always accompanied her, he thought of the young Queen, her mother, who but a short time before—so it seemed to him—had come from the gay country of France, and had withered away in the sombre splendour of the Spanish court, dying just six months after the birth of her child, and before she had seen the almonds blossom twice in the orchard, or plucked the second year's fruit from the old gnarled fig-tree that stood in the centre of the now grass-grown courtyard. So great had been his love for her that he had not suffered even the grave to hide her from him. She had been embalmed by a Moorish physician, who in return for this service had been granted his life, which for heresy and suspicion of magical practices had been already forfeited, men said, to the Holy Office, and her body was still lying on its tapestried bier in the black marble chapel of the Palace, just as the monks had borne her in on that windy March day nearly twelve years before. Once every month the King, wrapped in a dark cloak and with a muffled lantern in his hand, went in and knelt by her side calling out, 'Mi reina! Mi reina!' and sometimes breaking through the formal etiquette that in Spain governs every separate action of life, and sets limits even to the sorrow of a King, he would clutch at the pale jewelled hands in a wild agony of grief, and try to wake by his mad kisses the cold painted face.

To-day he seemed to see her again, as he had seen her first at the Castle of Fontainebleau, when he was but fifteen years of age, and she still younger. They had been formally betrothed on that occasion by the Papal Nuncio in the presence of the French King and all the Court, and he had returned to the Escurial bearing with him a little ringlet of yellow hair, and the memory of two childish lips bending down to kiss his hand as he stepped into his carriage. Later on had followed the marriage, hastily performed at Burgos, a small town on the frontier between the two countries, and the grand public entry into Madrid with the customary celebration of high mass at the Church of La Atocha, and a more than usually solemn auto-da-fé, in which nearly three hundred heretics, amongst whom were many Englishmen, had been delivered over to the secular arm to be burned.

Certainly he had loved her madly, and to the ruin, many thought, of his country, then at war with England for the possession of the empire of the New World. He had hardly ever permitted her to be out of his sight; for her, he had forgotten, or seemed to have forgotten, all grave affairs of State; and, with that terrible blindness that passion brings upon its servants, he had failed to notice that the elaborate ceremonies by which he sought to please her did but aggravate the strange malady from which she suffered. When she died he was, for a time, like one bereft of reason. Indeed, there is no doubt but that he would have formally abdicated and retired to the great Trappist monastery at Granada, of which he was already titular Prior, had he not been afraid to leave the little Infanta at the mercy of his brother, whose cruelty, even in Spain, was notorious, and who was suspected by many of having caused the Queen's death by means of a pair of poisoned gloves that he had presented to her on the occasion of her visiting his castle in Aragon. Even after the expiration of the three years of public mourning that he had ordained throughout his whole dominions by royal edict, he would never suffer his ministers to speak about any new alliance, and when the Emperor himself sent to him, and offered him the hand of the lovely Archduchess of Bohemia, his niece, in marriage, he bade the ambassadors tell their master that the King of Spain was already wedded to Sorrow, and that though she was but a barren bride he loved her better than Beauty; an answer that cost his crown the rich provinces of the Netherlands, which soon after, at the Emperor's instigation, revolted against him under the leadership of some fanatics of the Reformed Church.—*The Birthday of the Infranta.*

A BULL FIGHT

A procession of noble boys, fantastically dressed as toreadors, came out to meet her, and the young Count of Tierra-Nueva, a wonderfully handsome lad of about fourteen years of age, uncovering his head with all the grace of a born hidalgo and grandee of Spain, led her solemnly in to a little gilt and ivory chair that was placed on a raised dais above the arena. The children grouped themselves all round, fluttering their big fans and whispering to each other, and Don Pedro and the Grand Inquisitor stood laughing at the entrance. Even the Duchess—the Camerera-Mayor as she was called—a thin, hard-featured woman with a yellow ruff, did not look quite so bad-tempered as usual, and something like a chill smile flitted across her wrinkled face and twitched her thin bloodless lips.

It certainly was a marvellous bull-fight, and much nicer, the Infanta thought, than the real bull-fight that she had been brought to see at Seville, on the occasion of the visit of the Duke of Parma to her father. Some of the boys pranced about on richly-caparisoned hobby-horses brandishing long javelins with gay streamers of bright ribands attached to them; others went on foot waving their scarlet cloaks before the bull, and vaulting lightly over the barrier when he charged them; and as for the bull himself, he was just like a live bull, though he was only made of wicker-work and stretched hide, and sometimes insisted on running round the arena on his hind legs, which no live bull ever dreams of doing. He made a splendid fight of it too, and the children got so excited that they stood up upon the benches, and waved their lace handkerchiefs and cried out: Bravo toro! Bravo toro! just as sensibly as if they had been grown-up people. At last, however, after a prolonged combat, during which several of the hobby-horses were gored through and through, and, their riders dismounted, the young Count of Tierra-Nueva brought the bull to his knees, and having obtained permission from the Infanta to give the coup de grâce, he plunged his wooden sword into the neck of the animal with such violence that the head came right off, and disclosed the laughing face of little Monsieur de Lorraine, the son of the French Ambassador at Madrid.

The arena was then cleared amidst much applause, and the dead hobby-horses dragged solemnly away by two Moorish pages in yellow and black liveries, and after a short interlude, during which a French posture-master performed upon the tightrope, some Italian puppets appeared in the semi-classical tragedy of Sophonisba on the stage of a small theatre that had been built up for the purpose. They acted so well, and their gestures were so extremely natural, that at the close of the play the eyes of the Infanta were quite dim with tears. Indeed some of the children really cried, and had to be comforted with sweetmeats, and the Grand Inquisitor himself was so affected that he could not help saying to Don Pedro that it seemed to him intolerable that things made simply out of wood and coloured wax, and worked mechanically by wires, should be so unhappy and meet with such terrible misfortunes.—*The Birthday of the Infanta.*

THE THRONE ROOM

It was a throne-room, used for the reception of foreign ambassadors, when the King, which of late had not been often, consented to give them a personal audience; the same room in which, many years before, envoys had appeared from England to make arrangements for the marriage of their Queen, then one of the Catholic sovereigns of Europe, with the Emperor's eldest son. The hangings were of gilt Cordovan leather, and a heavy gilt chandelier with branches for three hundred wax lights hung down from the black and white ceiling. Underneath a great canopy of gold cloth, on which the lions and towers of Castile were broidered in seed pearls, stood the throne itself, covered with a rich pall of black velvet studded with silver tulips and laborately fringed with silver and pearls. On the second step of the throne was placed the kneeling-stool of the Infanta, with its cushion of cloth of silver issue, and below that again, and beyond the limit of the canopy, stood the chair for the Papal Nuncio, who alone had the right to be seated in the King's presence on the occasion of any public ceremonial, and whose Cardinal's hat, with its tangled scarlet tassels, lay on a purple tabouret in front. On the wall, facing the throne, hung a life-sized portrait of Charles V. in hunting dress, with a great mastiff by his side, and a picture of Philip II. receiving the homage of the Netherlands occupied the centre of the other wall. Between the windows stood a black ebony cabinet, inlaid with plates of ivory, on which the figures from Holbein's Dance of Death had been graved—by the hand, some said, of that famous master himself.

But the little Dwarf cared nothing for all this magnificence. He would not have given his rose for all the pearls on the canopy, nor one white petal of his rose for the throne itself. What he wanted was to see the Infanta before she went down to the pavilion, and to ask her to come away with him when he had finished his dance. Here, in the Palace, the air was close and heavy, but in the forest the wind blew free, and the sunlight with wandering hands of gold moved the tremulous leaves aside. There were flowers, too, in the forest, not so splendid, perhaps, as the flowers in the garden, but more sweetly scented for all that; hyacinths in early spring that flooded with waving purple the cool glens, and grassy knolls; yellow primroses that nestled in little clumps round the gnarled roots of the oak-trees; bright celandine, and blue speedwell, and irises lilac and gold. There were grey catkins on the hazels, and the foxgloves drooped with the weight of their dappled bee-haunted cells. The chestnut had its spires of white stars, and the hawthorn its pallid moons of beauty. Yes: surely she would come if he could only find her! She would come with him to the fair forest, and all day long he would dance for her delight. A smile lit up his eyes at the thought, and he passed into the next room.

Of all the rooms this was the brightest and the most beautiful. The walls were covered with a pink-flowered Lucca damask, patterned with birds and dotted with dainty blossoms of silver; the furniture was of massive silver, festooned with florid wreaths, and swinging Cupids; in front of the two large fire-places stood great screens broidered with parrots and peacocks, and the floor, which was of sea-green onyx, seemed to stretch far away into the distance. Nor was he alone. Standing under the shadow of the doorway, at the extreme end of the room, he saw a little figure watching him. His heart trembled, a cry of joy broke from his lips, and he moved out into the sunlight. As he did so, the figure moved out also, and he saw it plainly.— *The Birthday of the Infanta.*

A PROTECTED COUNTRY

'The kings of each city levied tolls on us, but would not suffer us to enter their gates. They threw us bread over the walls, little maize-cakes baked in honey and cakes of fine flour filled with dates. For every hundred baskets we gave them a bead of amber.

'When the dwellers in the villages saw us coming, they poisoned the wells and fled to the hill-summits. We fought with the Magadae who are born old, and grow younger and younger every year, and die when they are little children; and with the Laktroi who say that they are the sons of tigers, and paint themselves yellow and black; and with the Aurantes who bury their dead on the tops of trees, and themselves live in dark caverns lest the Sun, who is their god, should slay them; and with the Krimnians who worship a crocodile, and give it earrings of green glass, and feed it with butter and fresh fowls; and with the Agazonbae, who are dog-faced; and with the Sibans, who have horses' feet, and run more swiftly than horses. A third of our company died in battle, and a third died of want. The rest murmured against me, and said that I had brought them an evil fortune. I took a horned adder from beneath a stone and let it sting me. When they saw that I did not sicken they grew afraid.

'In the fourth month we reached the city of Illel. It was night-time when we came to the grove that is outside the walls, and the air was sultry, for the Moon was travelling in Scorpion. We took the ripe pomegranates from the trees, and brake them, and drank their sweet juices. Then we lay down on our carpets, and waited for the dawn.

'And at dawn we rose and knocked at the gate of the city. It was wrought out of red bronze, and carved with sea-dragons and dragons that have wings. The guards looked down from the battlements and asked us our business. The interpreter of the caravan answered that we had come from the island of Syria with much merchandise. They took hostages, and told us that they would open the gate to us at noon, and bade us tarry till then.

'When it was noon they opened the gate, and as we entered in the people came crowding out of the houses to look at us, and a crier went round the city crying through a shell. We stood in the market-place, and the negroes uncorded the bales of figured cloths and opened the carved chests of sycamore. And when they had ended their task, the merchants set forth their strange wares, the waxed linen from Egypt and the painted linen from the country of the Ethiops, the purple sponges from Tyre and the blue hangings from Sidon, the cups of cold amber and the fine vessels of glass and the curious vessels of burnt clay. From the roof of a house a company of women watched us. One of them wore a mask of gilded leather.

'And on the first day the priests came and bartered with us, and on the second day came the nobles, and on the third day came the craftsmen and the slaves. And this is their custom with all merchants as long as they tarry in the city.

'And we tarried for a moon, and when the moon was waning, I wearied and wandered away through the streets of the city and came to the garden of its god. The priests in their yellow robes moved silently through the green trees, and on a pavement of black marble stood the rose-red house in which the god had his dwelling. Its doors were of powdered lacquer, and bulls and peacocks were wrought on them in raised and polished gold. The tilted roof was of sea-green porcelain, and the jutting eaves were festooned with little bells. When the white doves flew past, they struck the bells with their wings and made them tinkle.

'In front of the temple was a pool of clear water paved with veined onyx. I lay down beside it, and with my pale fingers I touched the broad leaves. One of the priests came towards me and stood behind me. He had sandals on his feet, one of soft serpent-skin and the other of birds' plumage. On his head was a mitre of black felt decorated with silver crescents. Seven yellows were woven into his robe, and his frizzed hair was stained with antimony.

'After a little while he spake to me, and asked me my desire.

'I told him that my desire was to see the god.'—*The Fisherman and His Soul.*

THE BLACKMAILING OF THE EMPEROR

'As soon as the man was dead the Emperor turned to me, and when he had wiped away the bright sweat from his brow with a little napkin of purfled and purple silk, he said to me, "Art thou a prophet, that I may not harm thee, or the son of a prophet, that I can do thee no hurt? I pray thee leave my city to-night, for while thou art in it I am no longer its lord."

'And I answered him, "I will go for half of thy treasure. Give me half of thy treasure, and I will go away."

'He took me by the hand, and led me out into the garden. When the captain of the guard saw me, he wondered. When the eunuchs saw me, their knees shook and they fell upon the ground in fear.

'There is a chamber in the palace that has eight walls of red porphyry, and a brass-sealed ceiling hung with lamps. The Emperor touched one of the walls and it opened, and we passed down a corridor that was lit with many torches. In niches upon each side stood great wine-jars filled to the brim with silver pieces. When we reached the centre of the corridor the Emperor spake the word that may not be spoken, and a granite door swung back on a secret spring, and he put his hands before his face lest his eyes should be dazzled.

'Thou couldst not believe how marvellous a place it was. There were huge tortoise-shells full of pearls, and hollowed moonstones of great size piled up with red rubies. The gold was stored in coffers of elephant-hide, and the gold-dust in leather bottles. There were opals and sapphires, the former in cups of crystal, and the latter in cups of jade. Round green emeralds were ranged in order upon thin plates of ivory, and in one corner were silk bags filled, some with turquoise-stones, and others with beryls. The ivory horns were heaped with purple amethysts, and the horns of brass with chalcedonies and sards. The pillars, which were of cedar, were hung with strings of yellow lynx-stones. In the flat oval shields there were carbuncles, both wine-coloured and coloured like grass. And yet I have told thee but a tithe of what was there.

'And when the Emperor had taken away his hands from before his face he said to me: "This is my house of treasure, and half that is in it is thine, even as I promised to thee. And I will give thee camels and camel drivers, and they shall do thy bidding and take thy share of the treasure to whatever part of the world thou desirest to go. And the thing shall be done to-night, for I would not that the Sun, who is my father, should see that there is in my city a man whom I cannot slay."

'But I answered him, "The gold that is here is thine, and the silver also is thine, and thine are the precious jewels and the things of price. As for me, I have no need of these. Nor shall I take aught from thee but that little ring that thou wearest on the finger of thy hand."

'And the Emperor frowned. "It is but a ring of lead," he cried, "nor has it any value. Therefore take thy half of the treasure and go from my city."

'"Nay," I answered, "but I will take nought but that leaden ring, for I know what is written within it, and for what purpose."

'And the Emperor trembled, and besought me and said, "Take all the treasure and go from my city. The half that is mine shall be thine also."

'And I did a strange thing, but what I did matters not, for in a cave that is but a day's journey from this place have, I hidden the Ring of Riches. It is but a day's journey from this place, and it waits for thy coming. He who has this Ring is richer than all the kings of the world. Come therefore and take it, and the world's riches shall be thine.'—*The Fisherman and His Soul.*

COVENT GARDEN

Where he went he hardly knew. He had a dim memory of wandering through a labyrinth of sordid houses, of being lost in a giant web of sombre streets, and it was bright dawn when he found himself at last in Piccadilly Circus. As he strolled home towards Belgrave Square, he met the great waggons on their way to Covent Garden. The white-smocked carters, with their pleasant sunburnt faces and coarse curly hair, strode sturdily on, cracking their whips, and calling out now and then to each other; on the back of a huge grey horse, the leader of a jangling team, sat a chubby boy, with a bunch of primroses in his battered hat, keeping tight hold of the mane with his little hands, and laughing; and the great piles of vegetables looked like masses of jade against the morning sky, like masses of green jade against the pink petals of some marvellous rose. Lord Arthur felt curiously affected, he could not tell why. There was something in the dawn's delicate loveliness that seemed to him inexpressibly pathetic, and he thought of all the days that break in beauty, and that set in storm. These rustics, too, with their rough, good-humoured voices, and their nonchalant ways, what a strange London they saw! A London free from the sin of night and the smoke of day, a pallid, ghost-like city, a desolate town of tombs! He wondered what they thought of it, and whether they knew anything of its splendour and its shame, of its fierce, fiery-coloured joys, and its horrible hunger, of all it makes and mars from morn to eve. Probably it was to them merely a mart where they brought their fruits to sell, and where they tarried for a few hours at most, leaving the streets still silent, the houses still asleep. It gave him pleasure to watch them as they went by. Rude as they were, with their heavy, hob-nailed shoes, and their awkward gait, they brought a little of a ready with them. He felt that they had lived with Nature, and that she had taught them peace. He envied them all that they did not know.

By the time he had reached Belgrave Square the sky was a faint blue, and the birds were beginning to twitter in the gardens.—*Lord Arthur Savile's Crime.*

A LETTER FROM MISS JANE PERCY TO HER AUNT

THE DEANERY, CHICHESTER,

27th May.

My Dearest Aunt,

Thank you so much for the flannel for the Dorcas Society, and also for the gingham. I quite agree with you that it is nonsense their wanting to wear pretty things, but everybody is so Radical and irreligious nowadays, that it is difficult to make them see that they should not try and dress like the upper classes. I am sure I don't know what we are coming to. As papa has often said in his sermons, we live in an age of unbelief.

We have had great fun over a clock that an unknown admirer sent papa last Thursday. It arrived in a wooden box from London, carriage paid, and papa feels it must have been sent by some one who had read his remarkable sermon, 'Is Licence Liberty?' for on the top of the clock was a figure of a woman, with what papa said was the cap of Liberty on her head. I didn't think it very becoming myself, but papa said it was historical, so I suppose it is all right. Parker unpacked it, and papa put it on the mantelpiece in the library, and we were all sitting there on Friday morning, when just as the clock struck twelve, we heard a whirring noise, a little puff of smoke came from the pedestal of the figure, and the goddess of Liberty fell off, and broke her nose on the fender! Maria was quite alarmed, but it looked so ridiculous, that James and I went off into fits of laughter, and even papa was amused. When we examined it, we found it was a sort of alarum clock, and that, if you set it to a particular hour, and put some gunpowder and a cap under a little hammer, it went off whenever you wanted. Papa said it must not remain in the library, as it made a noise, so Reggie carried it away to the schoolroom, and does nothing but have small explosions all day long. Do you think Arthur would like one for a wedding present? I suppose they are quite fashionable in London. Papa says they should do a great deal of good, as they show that Liberty can't last, but must fall down. Papa says Liberty was invented at the time of the French Revolution. How awful it seems!

I have now to go to the Dorcas, where I will read them your most instructive letter. How true, dear aunt, your idea is, that in their rank of life they should wear what is unbecoming. I must say it is absurd, their anxiety about dress, when there are so many more important things in this world, and in the next. I am so glad your flowered poplin turned out so well, and that your lace was not torn. I am wearing my yellow satin, that you so kindly gave me, at the Bishop's on Wednesday, and think it will look all right. Would you have bows or not? Jennings says that every one wears bows now, and that the underskirt should be frilled. Reggie has just had another explosion, and papa has ordered the clock to be sent to the stables. I don't think papa likes it so much as he did at first, though he is very flattered at being sent such a pretty and ingenious toy. It shows that people read his sermons, and profit by them.

Papa sends his love, in which James, and Reggie, and Maria all unite and, hoping that Uncle Cecil's gout is better, believe me, dear aunt, ever your affectionate niece,

JANE PERCY.

PS.—Do tell me about the bows. Jennings insists they are the fashion.—
Lord Arthur Savile's Crime.

THE TRIUMPH OF AMERICAN 'HUMOR'

At half-past ten he heard the family going to bed. For some time he was disturbed by wild shrieks of laughter from the twins, who, with the light hearted gaiety of schoolboys, were evidently amusing themselves before they retired to rest, but at a quarter past eleven all was still, and, as midnight sounded, he sallied forth. The owl beat against the window panes, the raven croaked from the old yew-tree, and the wind wandered moaning round the house like a lost soul; but the Otis family slept unconscious of their doom, and high above the rain and storm he could hear the steady snoring of the Minister for the United States. He stepped stealthily out of the wainscoting, with an evil smile on his cruel, wrinkled mouth, and the moon hid her face in a cloud as he stole past the great oriel window, where his own arms and those of his murdered wife were blazoned in azure and gold. On and on he glided, like an evil shadow, the very darkness seeming to loathe him as he passed. Once he thought he heard something call, and stopped; but it was only the baying of a dog from the Red Farm, and he went on, muttering strange sixteenth-century curses, and ever and anon brandishing the rusty dagger in the midnight air. Finally he reached the corner of the passage that led to luckless Washington's room. For a moment he paused there, the wind blowing his long grey locks about his head, and twisting into grotesque and fantastic folds the nameless horror of the dead man's shroud. Then the clock struck the quarter, and he felt the time was come. He chuckled to himself, and turned the corner; but no sooner had he done so, than, with a

160

piteous wail of terror, he fell back, and hid his blanched face in his long, bony hands. Right in front of him was standing a horrible spectre, motionless as a carven image, and monstrous as a madman's dream! Its head was bald and burnished; its face round, and fat, and white; and hideous laughter seemed to have writhed its features into an eternal grin. From the eyes streamed rays of scarlet light, the mouth was a wide well of fire, and a hideous garment, like to his own, swathed with its silent snows the Titan form. On its breast was a placard with strange writing in antique characters, some scroll of shame it seemed, some record of wild sins, some awful calendar of crime, and, with its right hand, it bore aloft a falchion of gleaming steel.

Never having seen a ghost before, he naturally was terribly frightened, and, after a second hasty glance at the awful phantom, he fled back to his room, tripping up in his long winding-sheet as he sped down the corridor, and finally dropping the rusty dagger into the Minister's jack-boots, where it was found in the morning by the butler. Once in the privacy of his own apartment, he flung himself down on a small pallet-bed, and hid his face under the clothes. After a time, however, the brave old Canterville spirit asserted itself, and he determined to go and speak to the other ghost as soon as it was daylight. Accordingly, just as the dawn was touching the hills with silver, he returned towards the spot where he had first laid eyes on the grisly phantom, feeling that, after all, two ghosts were better than one, and that, by the aid of his new friend, he might safely grapple with the twins. On reaching the spot, however, a terrible sight met his gaze. Something had evidently happened to the spectre, for the light had entirely faded from its hollow eyes, the gleaming falchion had fallen from its hand, and it was leaning up against the wall in a strained and uncomfortable attitude. He rushed forward and seized it in his arms, when, to his horror, the head slipped off and rolled on the floor, the body assumed a recumbent posture, and he found himself clasping a white dimity bed-curtain, with a sweeping-brush, a kitchen cleaver, and a hollow turnip lying at his feet!—*The Canterville Ghost.*

THE GARDEN OF DEATH

'Far away beyond the pine-woods,' he answered, in a low dreamy voice, 'there is a little garden. There the grass grows long and deep, there are the great white stars of the hemlock flower, there the nightingale sings all night long. All night long he sings, and the cold, crystal moon looks down, and the yew-tree spreads out its giant arms over the sleepers.'

Virginia's eyes grew dim with tears, and she hid her face in her hands.

'You mean the Garden of Death,' she whispered.

'Yes, Death. Death must be so beautiful. To lie in the soft brown earth, with the grasses waving above one's head, and listen to silence. To have no yesterday, and no to-morrow. To forget time, to forgive life, to be at peace. You can help me. You can open for me the portals of Death's house, for Love is always with you, and Love is stronger than Death is.'

Virginia trembled, a cold shudder ran through her, and for a few moments there was silence. She felt as if she was in a terrible dream.

Then the Ghost spoke again, and his voice sounded like the sighing of the wind.

'Have you ever read the old prophecy on the library window?'

'Oh, often,' cried the little girl, looking up; 'I know it quite well. It is painted in curious black letters, and it is difficult to read. There are only six lines:

> When a golden girl can win
>
> Prayer from out the lips of sin,
>
> When the barren almond bears,
>
> And a little child gives away its tears,
>
> Then shall all the house be still
>
> And peace come to Canterville.

But I don't know what they mean.'

'They mean,' he said sadly, 'that you must weep for me for my sins, because I have no tears, and pray with me for my soul, because I have no faith, and then, if you have always been sweet, and good, and gentle, the Angel of Death will have mercy on me. You will see fearful shapes in darkness, and wicked voices will whisper in your ear, but they will not harm you, for against the purity of a little child the powers of Hell cannot prevail.'

Virginia made no answer, and the Ghost wrung his hands in wild despair as he looked down at her bowed golden head. Suddenly she stood up, very pale, and with a strange light in her eyes. 'I am not afraid,' she said firmly, 'and I will ask the Angel to have mercy on you.'

He rose from his seat with a faint cry of joy, and taking her hand bent over it with old-fashioned grace and kissed it. His fingers were as cold as ice, and his lips burned like fire, but Virginia did not falter, as he led her across the dusky room. On the faded green tapestry were broidered little huntsmen. They blew their tasselled horns and with their tiny hands waved to her to go back. 'Go back! little Virginia,' they cried, 'go back!' but the Ghost clutched her hand more tightly, and she shut her eyes against them. Horrible animals with lizard tails, and goggle eyes, blinked at her from the carven chimney-piece, and murmured 'Beware! little Virginia, beware! we may never see you again,' but the Ghost glided on more swiftly, and Virginia did not listen. When they reached the end of the room he stopped, and muttered some words she could not understand. She opened her eyes, and saw the wall slowly fading away like a mist, and a great black cavern in front of her. A bitter cold wind swept round them, and she felt something pulling at her dress. 'Quick, quick,' cried the Ghost, 'or it will be too late,' and, in a moment, the wainscoting had closed behind them, and the Tapestry Chamber was empty.—*The Canterville Ghost.*

AN ETON KIT-CAT

"Well," said Erskine, lighting a cigarette, "I must begin by telling you about Cyril Graham himself. He and I were at the same house at Eton. I was a year or two older than he was, but we were immense friends, and did all our work and all our play together. There was, of course, a good deal more play than work, but I cannot say that I am sorry for that. It is always an advantage not to have received a sound commercial education, and what I learned in the playing fields at Eton has been quite as useful to me as anything I was taught

163

at Cambridge. I should tell you that Cyril's father and mother were both dead. They had been drowned in a horrible yachting accident off the Isle of Wight. His father had been in the diplomatic service, and had married a daughter, the only daughter, in fact, of old Lord Crediton, who became Cyril's guardian after the death of his parents. I don't think that Lord Crediton cared very much for Cyril. He had never really forgiven his daughter for marrying a man who had not a title. He was an extraordinary old aristocrat, who swore like a costermonger, and had the manners of a farmer. I remember seeing him once on Speech-day. He growled at me, gave me a sovereign, and told me not to grow up 'a damned Radical' like my father. Cyril had very little affection for him, and was only too glad to spend most of his holidays with us in Scotland. They never really got on together at all. Cyril thought him a bear, and he thought Cyril effeminate. He was effeminate, I suppose, in some things, though he was a very good rider and a capital fencer. In fact he got the foils before he left Eton. But he was very languid in his manner, and not a little vain of his good looks, and had a strong objection to football. The two things that really gave him pleasure were poetry and acting. At Eton he was always dressing up and reciting Shakespeare, and when he went up to Trinity he became a member of the A.D.C. his first term. I remember I was always very jealous of his acting. I was absurdly devoted to him; I suppose because we were so different in some things. I was a rather awkward, weakly lad, with huge feet, and horribly freckled. Freckles run in Scotch families just as gout does in English families. Cyril used to say that of the two he preferred the gout; but he always set an absurdly high value on personal appearance, and once read a paper before our debating society to prove that it was better to be good-looking than to be good. He certainly was wonderfully handsome. People who did not like him, Philistines and college tutors, and young men reading for the Church, used to say that he was merely pretty; but there was a great deal more in his face than mere prettiness. I think he was the most splendid creature I ever saw, and nothing could exceed the grace of his movements, the charm of his manner. He fascinated everybody who was worth fascinating, and a great many people who were not. He was often wilful and petulant, and I used to think him dreadfully insincere. It was due, I think, chiefly to his inordinate desire to please. Poor Cyril! I told him once hat he was contented with very cheap triumphs, but he only laughed. He vas horribly spoiled. All charming people, I fancy, are spoiled. It is the secret of their attraction.

"However, I must tell you about Cyril's acting. You know that no uctresses are allowed to play at the A.D.C. At least they were not in my time. don't know how it is now. Well, of course, Cyril was always cast for the girls' parts, and when As You Like It was produced he played Rosalind. It was a marvellous performance. In fact, Cyril Graham was the only perfect Rosalind have ever seen. It would be impossible to describe to you the beauty, the delicacy, the refinement of the whole thing. It made an immense sensation, und the horrid little theatre, as it was then, was crowded every night. Even vhen I read the play now I can't help thinking of Cyril. It might have been vritten for him. The next term he took his degree, and came to London to ead for the diplomatic. But he never did any work. He spent his days in eading Shakespeare's Sonnets, and his evenings at the theatre. He was, of course, wild to go on the stage. It was all that I and Lord Crediton could do o prevent him. Perhaps if he had gone on the stage he would be alive now. t is always a silly thing to give advice, but to give good advice is absolutely atal. I hope you will never fall into that error. If you do, you will be sorry or it."—*The Portrait of Mr. W. H.*

MRS. ERLYNNE EXERCISES THE PREROGATIVE OF A GRANDMOTHER

Lady Windermere, before Heaven your husband is guiltless of all offence owards you! And I—I tell you that had it ever occurred to me that such a monstrous suspicion would have entered your mind, I would have died rather han have crossed your life or his—oh! died, gladly died! Believe what you choose about me. I am not worth a moment's sorrow. But don't spoil your beautiful young life on my account! You don't know what may be in store for ou, unless you leave this house at once. You don't know what it is to fall into he pit, to be despised, mocked, abandoned, sneered at—to be an outcast! to ind the door shut against one, to have to creep in by hideous byways, afraid very moment lest the mask should be stripped from one's face, and all the vhile to hear the laughter, the horrible laughter of the world, a thing more ragic than all the tears the world has ever shed. You don't know what it is.

One pays for one's sin, and then one pays again, and all one's life one pays. You must never know that.—As for me, if suffering be an expiation, then at this moment I have expiated all my faults, whatever they have been; for to-night you have made a heart in one who had it not, made it and broken it.—But let that pass. I may have wrecked my own life, but I will not let you wreck yours. You—why, you are a mere girl, you would be lost. You haven't got the kind of brains that enables a woman to get back. You have neither the wit nor the courage. You couldn't stand dishonour! No! Go back, Lady Windermere, to the husband who loves you, whom you love. You have a child, Lady Windermere. Go back to that child who even now, in pain or in joy, may be calling to you. God gave you that child. He will require from you that you make his life fine, that you watch over him. What answer will you make to God if his life is ruined through you? Back to your house, Lady Windermere—your husband loves you! He has never swerved for a moment from the love he bears you. But even if he had a thousand loves, you must stay with your child. If he was harsh to you, you must stay with your child. If he ill-treated you, you must stay with your child. If he abandoned you, your place is with your child.—*Lady Windermere's Fan.*

MOTHERHOOD MORE THAN MARRIAGE

Men don't understand what mothers are. I am no different from other women except in the wrong done me and the wrong I did, and my very heavy punishments and great disgrace. And yet, to bear you I had to look on death. To nurture you I had to wrestle with it. Death fought with me for you. All women have to fight with death to keep their children. Death, being childless, wants our children from us. Gerald, when you were naked I clothed you, when you were hungry I gave you food. Night and day all that long winter I tended you. No office is too mean, no care too lowly for the thing we women love—and oh! how I loved you. Not Hannah, Samuel more. And you needed love, for you were weakly, and only love could have kept you alive. Only love can keep any one alive. And boys are careless often and without thinking give pain, and we always fancy that when they come to man's estate and know us better they will repay us. But it is not so. The world draws them from our side, and they make friends with whom they are happier than they are with us, and have amusements from which we are barred, and interests that are not ours: and they are unjust to us often, for when they find life bitter they blame us for it, and when they find it sweet we do not taste its sweetness with them . . . You made many friends and went into their houses and were glad with them, and I, knowing my secret, did not dare to follow, but stayed at home and closed the door, shut out the sun and sat in darkness. What should I have done in honest households? My past was ever with me. . . . And you thought I didn't care for the pleasant things of life. I tell you I longed for them, but did not dare to touch them, feeling I had no right. You thought I was happier working amongst the poor. That was my mission, you imagined. It was not, but where else was I to go? The sick do not ask if the hand that smooths their pillow is pure, nor the dying care if the lips that touch their brow have known the kiss of sin. It was you I thought of all the time; I gave to them the love you did not need: lavished on them a love that was not theirs . . . And you thought I spent too much of my time in going to Church, and in Church duties. But where else could I turn? God's house is the only house where sinners are made welcome, and you were always in my heart, Gerald, too much in my heart. For, though day after day, at morn or evensong, I have knelt in God's house, I have never repented of my sin. How could I repent of my sin when you, my love, were its fruit! Even now that you are bitter to me I cannot repent. I do not. You are more to me than innocence. I would rather be your mother—oh! much rather!—than have been always pure . . . Oh, don't you see? don't you understand? It is my dishonour that has made you so dear to me. It is my disgrace that has bound you so closely to me. It is the price I paid for you—the price of soul and body—that makes me love you as I do. Oh, don't ask me to do this horrible thing. Child of my shame, be still the child of my shame!—*A Woman of No Importance.*

THE DAMNABLE IDEAL

Why can't you women love us, faults and all? Why do you place us on monstrous pedestals? We have all feet of clay, women as well as men; but when we men love women, we love them knowing their weaknesses, their follies, their imperfections, love them all the more, it may be, for that reason. It is not the perfect, but the imperfect, who have need of love. It is when we are wounded by our own hands, or by the hands of others, that

167

love should come to cure us—else what use is love at all? All sins, except a sin against itself, Love should forgive. All lives, save loveless lives, true Love should pardon. A man's love is like that. It is wider, larger, more human than a woman's. Women think that they are making ideals of men. What they are making of us are false idols merely. You made your false idol of me, and I had not the courage to come down, show you my wounds, tell you my weaknesses. I was afraid that I might lose your love, as I have lost it now. And so, last night you ruined my life for me—yes, ruined it! What this woman asked of me was nothing compared to what she offered to me. She offered security, peace, stability. The sin of my youth, that I had thought was buried, rose up in front of me, hideous, horrible, with its hands at my throat. I could have killed it for ever, sent it back into its tomb, destroyed its record, burned the one witness against me. You prevented me. No one but you, you know it. And now what is there before me but public disgrace, ruin, terrible shame, the mockery of the world, a lonely dishonoured life, a lonely dishonoured death, it may be, some day? Let women make no more ideals of men! let them not put them on alters and bow before them, or they may ruin other lives as completely as you—you whom I have so wildly loved—have ruined mine!—*An Ideal Husband.*

FROM A REJECTED PRIZE-ESSAY

Nations may not have missions but they certainly have functions. And the function of ancient Italy was not merely to give us what is statical in our institutions and rational in our law, but to blend into one elemental creed the spiritual aspirations of Aryan and of Semite. Italy was not a pioneer in intellectual progress, nor a motive power in the evolution of thought. The owl of the goddess of Wisdom traversed over the whole land and found nowhere a resting-place. The dove, which is the bird of Christ, flew straight to the city of Rome and the new reign began. It was the fashion of early Italian painters to represent in mediæval costume the soldiers who watched over the tomb of Christ, and this, which was the result of the frank anachronism of all true art, may serve to us as an allegory. For it was in vain that the Middle Ages strove to guard the buried spirit of progress. When the dawn of the Greek spirit arose, the sepulchre was empty, the grave-clothes laid aside. Humanity had risen from the dead.

168

The study of Greek, it has been well said, implies the birth of criticism, comparison and research. At the opening of that education of modern by ancient thought which we call the Renaissance, it was the words of Aristotle which sent Columbus sailing to the New World, while a fragment of Pythagorean astronomy set Copernicus thinking on that train of reasoning which has revolutionised the whole position of our planet in the universe. Then it was seen that the only meaning of progress is a return to Greek modes of thought. The monkish hymns which obscured the pages of Greek manuscripts were blotted out, the splendours of a new method were unfolded to the world, and out of the melancholy sea of mediævalism rose the free spirit of man in all that splendour of glad adolescence, when the bodily powers seem quickened by a new vitality, when the eye sees more clearly than its wont and the mind apprehends what was beforetime hidden from it. To herald the opening of the sixteenth century, from the little Venetian printing press came forth all the great authors of antiquity, each bearing on the title-page the words Αλδος ο Μανουτιος Ρωμαιος και Φιλελλην; words which may serve to remind us with what wondrous prescience Polybius saw the world's fate when he foretold the material sovereignty of Roman institutions and exemplified in himself the intellectual empire of Greece.

The course of the study of the spirit of historical criticism has not been a profitless investigation into modes and forms of thought now antiquated and of no account. The only spirit which is entirely removed from us is the mediæval; the Greek spirit is essentially modern. The introduction of the comparative method of research which has forced history to disclose its secrets belongs in a measure to us. Ours, too, is a more scientific knowledge of philology and the method of survival. Nor did the ancients know anything of the doctrine of averages or of crucial instances, both of which methods have proved of such importance in modern criticism, the one adding a most important proof of the statical elements of history, and exemplifying the influences of all physical surroundings on the life of man; the other, as in the single instance of the Moulin Quignon skull, serving to create a whole new science of prehistoric archæology and to bring us back to a time when man was coeval with the stone age, the mammoth and the woolly rhinoceros. But, except these, we have added no new canon or method to the science of historical criticism. Across the drear waste of a thousand years the Greek and the modern spirit join hands.

In the torch race which the Greek boys ran from the Cerameician field of death to the home of the goddess of Wisdom, not merely he who first reached the goal but he also who first started with the torch aflame received a prize. In the Lampadephoria of civilisation and free thought let us not forget to render due meed of honour to those who first lit that sacred flame, the increasing splendour of which lights our footsteps to the far-off divine event of the attainment of perfect truth.—*The Rise of Historical Criticism.*

THE POSSIBILITIES OF THE USEFUL

There are two kinds of men in the world, two great creeds, two different forms of natures: men to whom the end of life is action, and men to whom the end of life is thought. As regards the latter, who seek for experience itself and not for the fruits of experience, who must burn always with one of the passions of this fiery-coloured world, who find life interesting not for its secret but for its situations, for its pulsations and not for its purpose; the passion for beauty engendered by the decorative arts will be to them more satisfying than any political or religious enthusiasm, any enthusiasm for humanity, any ecstasy or sorrow for love. For art comes to one professing primarily to give nothing but the highest quality to one's moments, and for those moments' sake. So far for those to whom the end of life is thought. As regards the others, who hold that life is inseparable from labour, to them should this movement be specially dear: for, if our days are barren without industry, industry without art is barbarism.

Hewers of wood and drawers of water there must be always indeed among us. Our modern machinery has not much lightened the labour of man after all: but at least let the pitcher that stands by the well be beautiful and surely the labour of the day will be lightened: let the wood be made receptive of some lovely form, some gracious design, and there will come no longer discontent but joy to the toiler. For what is decoration but the worker's expression of joy in his work? And not joy merely—that is a great thing yet not enough—but that opportunity of expressing his own individuality which, as it is the essence of all life, is the source of all art. 'I have tried,' I

170

emember William Morris saying to me once, 'I have tried to make each of ny workers an artist, and when I say an artist I mean a man.' For the worker hen, handicraftsman of whatever kind he is, art is no longer to be a purple obe woven by a slave and thrown over the whitened body of a leprous king o hide and to adorn the sin of his luxury, but rather the beautiful and noble xpression of a life that has in it something beautiful and noble.—*The English Renaissance of Art.*

THE ARTIST

ONE evening there came into his soul the desire to fashion an image of *The Pleasure that abideth for a Moment.* And he went forth into the world to ook for bronze. For he could think only in bronze.

But all the bronze of the whole world had disappeared, nor anywhere in he whole world was there any bronze to be found, save only the bronze of the mage of *The Sorrow that endureth for Ever.*

Now this image he had himself, and with his own hands, fashioned, and ad set it on the tomb of the one thing he had loved in life. On the tomb of he dead thing he had most loved had he set this image of his own fashioning, hat it might serve as a sign of the love of man that dieth not, and a symbol of he sorrow of man that endureth for ever. And in the whole world there was o other bronze save the bronze of this image.

And he took the image he had fashioned, and set it in a great furnace, nd gave it to the fire.

And out of the bronze of the image of *The Sorrow that endureth for Ever* e fashioned an image of *The Pleasure that abideth for a Moment.—Poems in Prose.*

THE DOER OF GOOD

It was night-time and He was alone.

And He saw afar-off the walls of a round city and went towards the city.

And when He came near He heard within the city the tread of the feet f joy, and the laughter of the mouth of gladness and the loud noise of many lutes. And He knocked at the gate and certain of the gate-keepers opened to Him.

And He beheld a house that was of marble and had fair pillars of marbl before it. The pillars were hung with garlands, and within and without ther were torches of cedar. And He entered the house.

And when He had passed through the hall of chalcedony and the hal of jasper, and reached the long hall of feasting, He saw lying on a couch o sea-purple one whose hair was crowned with red roses and whose lips wer red with wine.

And He went behind him and touched him on the shoulder and said t him, 'Why do you live like this?'

And the young man turned round and recognised Him, and mad answer and said, 'But I was a leper once, and you healed me. How els should I live?'

And He passed out of the house and went again into the street.

And after a little while He saw one whose face and raiment were painte and whose feet were shod with pearls. And behind her came, slowly as hunter, a young man who wore a cloak of two colours. Now the face of th woman was as the fair face of an idol, and the eyes of the young man wer bright with lust.

And He followed swiftly and touched the hand of the young man an said to him, 'Why do you look at this woman and in such wise?'

And the young man turned round and recognised Him and said, 'But was blind once, and you gave me sight. At what else should I look?'

And He ran forward and touched the painted raiment of the woma and said to her, 'Is there no other way in which to walk save the way of sin?'

And the woman turned round and recognised Him, and laughed an said, 'But you forgave me my sins, and the way is a pleasant way.'

And He passed out of the city.

172

And when He had passed out of the city He saw seated by the roadside a young man who was weeping.

And He went towards him and touched the long locks of his hair and said to him, 'Why are you weeping?'

And the young man looked up and recognised Him and made answer, 'But I was dead once, and you raised me from the dead. What else should I do but weep?'—*Poems in Prose.*

THE DISCIPLE

When Narcissus died the pool of his pleasure changed from a cup of sweet waters into a cup of salt tears, and the Oreads came weeping through the woodland that they might sing to the pool and give it comfort.

And when they saw that the pool had changed from a cup of sweet waters into a cup of salt tears, they loosened the green tresses of their hair and cried to the pool and said, 'We do not wonder that you should mourn in this manner for Narcissus, so beautiful was he.'

'But was Narcissus beautiful?' said the pool.

'Who should know that better than you?' answered the Oreads. 'Us did he ever pass by, but you he sought for, and would lie on your banks and look down at you, and in the mirror of your waters he would mirror his own beauty.'

And the pool answered, 'But I loved Narcissus because, as he lay on my banks and looked down at me, in the mirror of his eyes I saw ever my own beauty mirrored.'—*Poems in Prose.*

THE MASTER

Now when the darkness came over the earth Joseph of Arimathea, having lighted a torch of pinewood, passed down from the hill into the valley. For he had business in his own home.

And kneeling on the flint stones of the Valley of Desolation he saw a young man who was naked and weeping. His hair was the colour of honey, and his body was as a white flower, but he had wounded his body with thorns and on his hair had he set ashes as a crown.

And he who had great possessions said to the young man who was naked and weeping, 'I do not wonder that your sorrow is so great, for surely He was a just man.'

And the young man answered, 'It is not for Him that I am weeping, but for myself. I too have changed water into wine, and I have healed the leper and given sight to the blind. I have walked upon the waters, and from the dwellers in the tombs I have cast out devils. I have fed the hungry in the desert where there was no food, and I have raised the dead from their narrow houses, and at my bidding, and before a great multitude, of people, a barren fig-tree withered away. All things that this man has done I have done also. And yet they have not crucified me.'—*Poems in Prose.*

THE HOUSE OF JUDGMENT

And there was silence in the House of Judgment, and the Man came naked before God.

And God opened the Book of the Life of the Man.

And God said to the Man, 'Thy life hath been evil, and thou hast shown cruelty to those who were in need of succour, and to those who lacked help thou hast been bitter and hard of heart. The poor called to thee and thou didst not hearken, and thine ears were closed to the cry of My afflicted. The inheritance of the fatherless thou didst take unto thyself, and thou didst send the foxes into the vineyard of thy neighbour's field. Thou didst take the bread of the children and give it to the dogs to eat, and My lepers who lived in the marshes, and were at peace and praised Me, thou didst drive forth on to the highways, and on Mine earth out of which I made thee thou didst spill innocent blood.'

And the Man made answer and said, 'Even so did I.'

And again God opened the Book of the Life of the Man.

And God said to the Man, 'Thy life hath been evil, and the Beauty I have shown thou hast sought for, and the Good I have hidden thou didst pass by. The walls of thy chamber were painted with images, and from the bed of thine abominations thou didst rise up to the sound of flutes. Thou didst build seven altars to the sins I have suffered, and didst eat of the thing that may not be eaten, and the purple of thy raiment was broidered with the three signs of shame. Thine idols were neither of gold nor of silver that endure, but of flesh that dieth. Thou didst stain their hair with perfumes and put pomegranates in their hands. Thou didst stain their feet with saffron and spread carpets before them. With antimony thou didst stain their eyelids and their bodies thou didst smear with myrrh. Thou didst bow thyself to the ground before them, and the thrones of thine idols were set in the sun. Thou didst show to the sun thy shame and to the moon thy madness.'

And the Man made answer and said, 'Even so did I.'

And a third time God opened the Book of the Life of the Man.

And God said to the Man, 'Evil hath been thy life, and with evil didst thou requite good, and with wrongdoing kindness. The hands that fed thee thou didst wound, and the breasts that gave thee suck thou didst despise. He who came to thee with water went away thirsting, and the outlawed men who hid thee in their tents at night thou didst betray before dawn. Thine enemy who spared thee thou didst snare in an ambush, and the friend who walked with thee thou didst sell for a price, and to those who brought thee Love thou didst ever give Lust in thy turn.'

And the Man made answer and said, 'Even so did I.'

And God closed the Book of the Life of the Man, and said, 'Surely I will send thee into Hell. Even into Hell will I send thee.'

And the Man cried out, 'Thou canst not.'

And God said to the Man, 'Wherefore can I not send thee to Hell, and for what reason?'

'Because in Hell have I always lived,' answered the Man.

And there was silence in the House of Judgment.

And after a space God spake, and said to the Man, 'Seeing that I may

175

not send thee into Hell, surely I will send thee unto Heaven. Even unto Heaven will I send thee.'

And the Man cried out, 'Thou canst not.'

And God said to the Man, 'Wherefore can I not send thee unto Heaven, and for what reason?'

'Because never, and in no place, have I been able to imagine it,' answered the Man.

And there was silence in the House of Judgment.—*Poems in Prose.*

THE TEACHER OF WISDOM

From his childhood he had been as one filled with the perfect knowledge of God, and even while he was yet but a lad many of the saints, as well as certain holy women who dwelt in the free city of his birth, had been stirred to much wonder by the grave wisdom of his answers.

And when his parents had given him the robe and the ring of manhood he kissed them, and left them and went out into the world, that he might speak to the world about God. For there were at that time many in the world who either knew not God at all, or had but an incomplete knowledge of Him, or worshipped the false gods who dwell in groves and have no care of their worshippers.

And he set his face to the sun and journeyed, walking without sandals, as he had seen the saints walk, and carrying at his girdle a leathern wallet and a little water-bottle of burnt clay.

And as he walked along the highway he was full of the joy that comes from the perfect knowledge of God, and he sang praises unto God without ceasing; and after a time he reached a strange land in which there were many cities.

And he passed through eleven cities. And some of these cities were in valleys, and others were by the banks of great rivers, and others were set on hills. And in each city he found a disciple who loved him and followed him, and a great multitude also of people followed him from each city, and the

176

nowledge of God spread in the whole land, and many of the rulers were onverted, and the priests of the temples in which there were idols found that alf of their gain was gone, and when they beat upon their drums at noon one, or but a few, came with peacocks and with offerings of flesh as had been he custom of the land before his coming.

Yet the more the people followed him, and the greater the number of is disciples, the greater became his sorrow. And he knew not why his sorrow was so great. For he spake ever about God, and out of the fulness of that erfect knowledge of God which God had Himself given to him.

And one evening he passed out of the eleventh city, which was a city of rmenia, and his disciples and a great crowd of people followed after him; nd he went up on to a mountain and sat down on a rock that was on the nountain, and his disciples stood round him, and the multitude knelt in the alley.

And he bowed his head on his hands and wept, and said to his Soul, Why is it that I am full of sorrow and fear, and that each of my disciples is n enemy that walks in the noonday?' And his Soul answered him and said, God filled thee with the perfect knowledge of Himself, and thou hast given his knowledge away to others. The pearl of great price thou hast divided, nd the vesture without seam thou hast parted asunder. He who giveth away visdom robbeth himself. He is as one who giveth his treasure to a robber. Is ot God wiser than thou art? Who art thou to give away the secret that God ath told thee? I was rich once, and thou hast made me poor. Once I saw God, and now thou hast hidden Him from me.'

And he wept again, for he knew that his Soul spake truth to him, and hat he had given to others the perfect knowledge of God, and that he was as ne clinging to the skirts of God, and that his faith was leaving him by reason f the number of those who believed in him.

And he said to himself, 'I will talk no more about God. He who giveth way wisdom robbeth himself.'

And after the space of some hours his disciples came near him and bowed themselves to the ground and said, 'Master, talk to us about God for thou hast the perfect knowledge of God, and no man save thee hath this knowledge.'

And he answered them and said, 'I will talk to you about all other thing that are in heaven and on earth, but about God I will not talk to you. Neither now, nor at any time, will I talk to you about God.'

And they were wroth with him and said to him, 'Thou hast led us into the desert that we might hearken to thee. Wilt thou send us away hungry and the great multitude that thou hast made to follow thee?'

And he answered them and said, 'I will not talk to you about God.'

And the multitude murmured against him and said to him, 'Thou has led us into the desert, and hast given us no food to eat. Talk to us about God and it will suffice us.'

But he answered them not a word. For he knew that if he spake to them about God he would give away his treasure.

And his disciples went away sadly, and the multitude of people returned to their own homes. And many died on the way.

And when he was alone he rose up and set his face to the moon, and journeyed for seven moons, speaking to no man nor making any answer. And when the seventh moon had waned he reached that desert which is the desert of the Great River. And having found a cavern in which a Centaur had once dwelt, he took it for his place of dwelling, and made himself a mat of reed on which to lie, and became a hermit. And every hour the Hermit praised God that He had suffered him to keep some knowledge of Him and of His wonderful greatness.

Now, one evening, as the Hermit was seated before the cavern in which he had made his place of dwelling, he beheld a young man of evil and beautiful face who passed by in mean apparel and with empty hands. Every evening with empty hands the young man passed by, and every morning he returned with his hands full of purple and pearls. For he was a Robber and robbed the caravans of the merchants.

And the Hermit looked at him and pitied him. But he spake not a word. For he knew that he who speaks a word loses his faith.

And one morning, as the young man returned with his hands full of purple and pearls, he stopped and frowned and stamped his foot upon the sand, and said to the Hermit: 'Why do you look at me ever in this manner as I pass by? What is it that I see in your eyes? For no man has looked at me before in this manner. And the thing is a thorn and a trouble to me.'

And the Hermit answered him and said, 'What you see in my eyes is pity. Pity is what looks out at you from my eyes.'

And the young man laughed with scorn, and cried to the Hermit in a bitter voice, and said to him, 'I have purple and pearls in my hands, and you have but a mat of reeds on which to lie. What pity should you have for me? And for what reason have you this pity?'

'I have pity for you,' said the Hermit, 'because you have no knowledge of God.'

'Is this knowledge of God a precious thing?' asked the young man, and he came close to the mouth of the cavern.

'It is more precious than all the purple and the pearls of the world,' answered the Hermit.

'And have you got it?' said the young Robber, and he came closer still.

'Once, indeed,' answered the Hermit, 'I possessed the perfect knowledge of God. But in my foolishness I parted with it, and divided it amongst others. Yet even now is such knowledge as remains to me more precious than purple or pearls.'

And when the young Robber heard this he threw away the purple and the pearls that he was bearing in his hands, and drawing a sharp sword of curved steel he said to the Hermit, 'Give me, forthwith this knowledge of God that you possess, or I will surely slay you. Wherefore should I not slay him who has a treasure greater than my treasure?'

And the Hermit spread out his arms and said, 'Were it not better for me to go unto the uttermost courts of God and praise Him, than to live in the world and have no knowledge of Him? Slay me if that be your desire. But I will not give away my knowledge of God.'

And the young Robber knelt down and besought him, but the Hermit would not talk to him about God, nor give him his Treasure, and the young Robber rose up and said to the Hermit, 'Be it as you will. As for myself, I will go to the City of the Seven Sins, that is but three days' journey from this place, and for my purple they will give me pleasure, and for my pearls they will sell me joy.' And he took up the purple and the pearls and went swiftly away.

And the Hermit cried out and followed him and besought him. For the space of three days he followed the young Robber on the road and entreated him to return, nor to enter into the City of the Seven Sins.

And ever and anon the young Robber looked back at the Hermit and called to him, and said, 'Will you give me this knowledge of God which is more precious than purple and pearls? If you will give me that, I will not enter the city.'

And ever did the Hermit answer, 'All things that I have I will give thee, save that one thing only. For that thing it is not lawful for me to give away.'

And in the twilight of the third day they came nigh to the great scarlet gates of the City of the Seven Sins. And from the city there came the sound of much laughter.

And the young Robber laughed in answer, and sought to knock at the gate. And as he did so the Hermit ran forward and caught him by the skirts of his raiment, and said to him: 'Stretch forth your hands, and set your arms around my neck, and put your ear close to my lips, and I will give you what remains to me of the knowledge of God.' And the young Robber stopped.

And when the Hermit had given away his knowledge of God, he fell upon the ground and wept, and a great darkness hid from him the city and the young Robber, so that he saw them no more.

And as he lay there weeping he was ware of One who was standing beside him; and He who was standing beside him had feet of brass and hair like fine wool. And He raised the Hermit up, and said to him: 'Before this time thou hadst the perfect knowledge of God. Now thou shalt have the perfect love of God. Wherefore art thou weeping?' And he kissed him.—*Poems in Prose.*

WILDE GIVES DIRECTIONS ABOUT 'DE PROFUNDIS'

H.M. PRISON, READING.

April 1st, 1897.

My Dear Robbie,—I send you a MS. separate from this, which I hope will arrive safely. As soon as you have read it, I want you to have it carefully copied for me. There are many causes why I wish this to be done. One will suffice. I want you to be my literary executor in case of my death, and to have complete control of my plays, books, and papers. As soon as I find I have a legal right to make a will, I will do so. My wife does not understand my art, nor could be expected to have any interest in it, and Cyril is only a child. So I turn naturally to you, as indeed I do for everything, and would like you to have all my works. The deficit that their sale will produce may be lodged to the credit of Cyril and Vivian. Well, if you are my literary executor, you must be in possession of the only document that gives any explanation of my extraordinary behaviour . . . When you have read the letter, you will see the psychological explanation of a course of conduct that from the outside seems a combination of absolute idiotcy with vulgar bravado. Some day the truth will have to be known—not necessarily in my lifetime . . . but I am not prepared to sit in the grotesque pillory they put me into, for all time; for the simple reason that I inherited from my father and mother a name of high distinction in literature and art, and I cannot for eternity allow that name to be degraded. I don't defend my conduct. I explain it. Also there are in my letter certain passages which deal with my mental development in prison, and the inevitable evolution of my character and intellectual attitude towards life that has taken place: and I want you and others who still stand by me and have affection for me to know exactly in what mood and manner I hope to face the world. Of course from one point of view I know that on the day of my release I shall be merely passing from one prison into another, and there are times when the whole world seems to me no larger than my cell and as full of terror for me. Still I believe that at the beginning God made a world for each separate man, and in that world which is within us we should seek to live. At any rate you will read those parts of my letter with less pain than the others. Of course I need not remind you how fluid a thing thought is with me—with us all—and of what an evanescent substance are our emotions made. Still I do see a sort of possible goal towards which, through art, I may progress. It is not unlikely that you may help me.

As regards the mode of copying: of course it is too long for any amanuensis to attempt: and your own handwriting, dear Robbie, in your last letter seems specially designed to remind me that the task is not to be yours. I think that the only thing to do is to be thoroughly modern and to have it typewritten. Of course the MS. should not pass out of your control, but could you not get Mrs. Marshall to send down one of her type-writing girls—women are the most reliable as they have no memory for the important—to Hornton Street or Phillimore Gardens, to do it under your supervision? I assure you that the typewriting machine, when played with expression, is not more annoying than the piano when played by a sister or near relation. Indeed many among those most devoted to domesticity prefer it. I wish the copy to be done not on tissue paper but on good paper such as is used for plays, and a wide rubricated margin should be left for corrections . . . If the copy is done at Hornton Street the lady typewriter might be fed through a lattice in the door like the Cardinals when they elect a Pope; till she comes out on the balcony and can say to the world: "Habet Mundus Epistolam"; for indeed it is an Encyclical letter, and as the Bulls of the Holy Father are named from their opening words, it may be spoken of as the "Epistola: in Carcere et Vinculis." . . . In point of fact, Robbie, prison life makes one see people and things as they really are. That is why it turns one to stone. It is the people outside who are deceived by the illusions of a life in constant motion. They revolve with life and contribute to its unreality. We who are immobile both see and know. Whether or not the letter does good to narrow natures and hectic brains, t ne it has done good. I have "cleansed my bosom of much perilous stuff"; o borrow a phrase from the poet whom you and I once thought of rescuing rom the Philistines. I need not remind you that mere expression is to an rtist the supreme and only mode of life. It is by utterance that we live. Of he many, many things for which I have to thank the Governor there is none or which I am more grateful than for his permission to write fully and at as reat a length as I desire. For nearly two years I had within a growing burden f bitterness, of much of which I have now got rid. On the other side of he prison wall there are some poor black soot-besmirched trees that are just reaking out into buds of an almost shrill green. I know quite well what they re going through. They are finding expression.

Ever yours,

OSCAR.

—Letter from Reading Prison to Robert Ross.

CAREY STREET

Where there is sorrow there in holy ground. Some day people will realise what that means. They will know nothing of life till they do,—and natures ike his can realise it. When I was brought down from my prison to the Court f Bankruptcy, between two policemen,—waited in the long dreary corridor hat, before the whole crowd, whom an action so sweet and simple hushed nto silence, he might gravely raise his hat to me, as, handcuffed and with owed head, I passed him by. Men have gone to heaven for smaller things han that. It was in this spirit, and with this mode of love, that the saints knelt down to wash the feet of the poor, or stooped to kiss the leper on the heek. I have never said one single word to him about what he did. I do not know to the present moment whether he is aware that I was even conscious of is action. It is not a thing for which one can render formal thanks in formal words. I store it in the treasure-house of my heart. I keep it there as a secret debt that I am glad to think I can never possibly repay. It is embalmed and kept sweet by the myrrh and cassia of many tears. When wisdom has been rofitless to me, philosophy barren, and the proverbs and phrases of those who have sought to give me consolation as dust and ashes in my mouth, the

183

memory of that little, lovely, silent act of love has unsealed for me all th
wells of pity: made the desert blossom like a rose, and brought me out of th
bitterness of lonely exile into harmony with the wounded, broken, and gre
heart of the world. When people are able to understand, not merely ho
beautiful ---'s action was, but why it meant so much to me, and always w
mean so much, then, perhaps, they will realise how and in what spirit the
should approach me. . . .

The poor are wise, more charitable, more kind, more sensitive than w
are. In their eyes prison is a tragedy in a man's life, a misfortune, a casualit
something that calls for sympathy in others. They speak of one who is i
prison as of one who is 'in trouble' simply. It is the phrase they always us
and the expression has the perfect wisdom of love in it. With people of o
own rank it is different. With us, prison makes a man a pariah. I, and such
I am, have hardly any right to air and sun. Our presence taints the pleasur
of others. We are unwelcome when we reappear. To revisit the glimpses
the moon is not for us. Our very children are taken away. Those lovely lin
with humanity are broken. We are doomed to be solitary, while our sons st
live. We are denied the one thing that might heal us and keep us, that mig
bring balm to the bruised heart, and peace to the soul in pain.—*De Profund*

SORROW WEARS NO MASK

Sorrow, being the supreme emotion of which man is capable, is at on
the type and test of all great art. What the artist is always looking for is th
mode of existence in which soul and body are one and indivisible: in whic
the outward is expressive of the inward: in which form reveals. Of suc
modes of existence there are not a few: youth and the arts preoccupied wit
youth may serve as a model for us at one moment: at another we may like
think that, in its subtlety and sensitiveness of impression, its suggestion of
spirit dwelling in external things and making its raiment of earth and air,
mist and city alike, and in its morbid sympathy of its moods, and tones, an
colours, modern landscape art is realising for us pictorially what was realised
such plastic perfection by the Greeks. Music, in which all subject is absorbe
in expression and cannot be separated from it, is a complex example, and
flower or a child a simple example, of what I mean; but sorrow is the ultima

type both in life and art.

Behind joy and laughter there may be a temperament, coarse, hard and callous. But behind sorrow there is always sorrow. Pain, unlike pleasure, wears no mask. Truth in art is not any correspondence between the essential idea and the accidental existence; it is not the resemblance of shape to shadow, or of the form mirrored in the crystal to the form itself; it is no echo coming from a hollow hill, any more than it is a silver well of water in the valley that shows the moon to the moon and Narcissus to Narcissus. Truth in art is the unity of a thing with itself: the outward rendered expressive of the inward: the soul made incarnate: the body instinct with spirit. For this reason there is no truth comparable to sorrow. There are times when sorrow seems to me to be the only truth. Other things may be illusions of the eye or the appetite, made to blind the one and cloy the other, but out of sorrow have the worlds been built, and at the birth of a child or a star there is pain.

More than this, there is about sorrow an intense, an extraordinary reality. I have said of myself that I was one who stood in symbolic relations to the art and culture of my age. There is not a single wretched man in this wretched place along with me who does not stand in symbolic relation to the very secret of life. For the secret of life is suffering. It is what is hidden behind everything. When we begin to live, what is sweet is so sweet to us, and what is bitter so bitter, that we inevitably direct all our desires towards pleasures, and seek not merely for a 'month or twain to feed on honeycomb,' but for all our years to taste no other food, ignorant all the while that we may really be starving the soul.—*De Profundis.*

VITA NUOVA

Far off, like a perfect pearl, one can see the city of God. It is so wonderful that it seems as if a child could reach it in a summer's day. And so a child could. But with me and such as me it is different. One can realise a thing in a single moment, but one loses it in the long hours that follow with leaden feet. It is so difficult to keep 'heights that the soul is competent to gain.' We think in eternity, but we move slowly through time; and how slowly time goes with us who lie in prison I need not tell again, nor of the weariness and despair that creep back into one's cell, and into the cell of one's heart, with such strange insistence that one has, as it were, to garnish and sweep one's house for their coming, as for an unwelcome guest, or a bitter master, or a slave whose slave it is one's chance or choice to be.

And, though at present my friends may find it a hard thing to believe, it is true none the less, that for them living in freedom and idleness and comfort it is more easy to learn the lessons of humility than it is for me, who begin the day by going down on my knees and washing the floor of my cell. For prison life with its endless privations and restrictions makes one rebellious. The most terrible thing about it is not that it breaks one's heart—hearts are made to be broken—but that it turns one's heart to stone. One sometimes feels that it is only with a front of brass and a lip of scorn that one can get through the day at all. And he who is in a state of rebellion cannot receive grace, to use the phrase of which the Church is so fond—so rightly fond, I dare say—for in life as in art the mood of rebellion closes up the channels of the soul, and shuts out the airs of heaven. Yet I must learn these lessons here, if I am to learn them anywhere, and must be filled with joy if my feet are on the right road and my face set towards 'the gate which is called beautiful,' though I may fall many times in the mire and often in the mist go astray.

This New Life, as through my love of Dante I like sometimes to call it, is of course no new life at all, but simply the continuance, by means of development, and evolution, of my former life. I remember when I was at Oxford saying to one of my friends as we were strolling round Magdalen's narrow bird-haunted walks one morning in the year before I took my degree, that I wanted to eat of the fruit of all the trees in the garden of the world, and that I was going out into the world with that passion in my soul. And so, indeed, I went out, and so I lived. My only mistake was that I confined myself so exclusively to the trees of what seemed to me the sun-lit side of the garden, and shunned the other side for its shadow and its gloom. Failure, disgrace, poverty, sorrow, despair, suffering, tears even, the broken words that come from lips in pain, remorse that makes one walk on thorns, conscience that condemns, self-abasement that punishes, the misery that puts ashes on its head, the anguish that chooses sack-cloth for its raiment and into its own drink puts gall:—all these were things of which I was afraid. And as I had determined to know nothing of them, I was forced to taste each of them in turn, to feed on them, to have for a season, indeed, no other food at all.

I don't regret for a single moment having lived for pleasure. I did it to the full, as one should do everything that one does. There was no pleasure I did not experience. I threw the pearl of my soul into a cup of wine. I went down the primrose path to the sound of flutes. I lived on honeycomb. But to have continued the same life would have been wrong because it would have been limiting. I had to pass on. The other half of the garden had its secrets for me also.—*De Profundis.*

THE GRAND ROMANTIC

It is when he deals with a sinner that Christ is most romantic, in the sense of most real. The world had always loved the saint as being the nearest possible approach to the perfection of God. Christ, through some divine instinct in him, seems to have always loved the sinner as being the nearest possible approach to the perfection of man. His primary desire was not to reform people, any more than his primary desire was to a relieve suffering. To turn an interesting thief into a tedious honest man was not his aim. He would have thought little of the Prisoners' Aid Society and other modern movements of the kind. The conversion of a publican into a Pharisee would not have seemed to him a great achievement. But in a manner not yet understood of the world he regarded sin and suffering as being in themselves beautiful holy things and modes of perfection.

It seems a very dangerous idea. It is—all great ideas are dangerous. That it was Christ's creed admits of no doubt. That it is the true creed I don't doubt myself.

Of course the sinner must repent. But why? Simply because otherwise he would be unable to realise what he had done. The moment of repentance is the moment of initiation. More than that: it is the means by which one alters one's past. The Greeks thought that impossible. They often say in their Gnomic aphorisms, 'Even the Gods cannot alter the past.' Christ showed that the commonest sinner could do it, that it was the one thing he could do. Christ, had he been asked, would have said—I feel quite certain about it—that the moment the prodigal son fell on his knees and wept, he made his having wasted his substance with harlots, his swine-herding and hungering for the husks they ate, beautiful and holy moments in his life. It is difficult for most people to grasp the idea. I dare say one has to go to prison to understand it. If so, it may be worth while going to prison.

There is something so unique about Christ. Of course just as there are false dawns before the dawn itself, and winter days so full of sudden sunlight that they will cheat the wise crocus into squandering its gold before its time, and make some foolish bird call to its mate to build on barren boughs, so there were Christians before Christ. For that we should be grateful. The unfortunate thing is that there have been none since. I make one exception, St. Francis of Assisi. But then God had given him at his birth the soul of a poet, as he himself when quite young had in mystical marriage taken poverty as his bride: and with the soul of a poet and the body of a beggar he found the way to perfection not difficult. He understood Christ, and so he became like him. We do not require the Liber Conformitatum to teach us that the life of St. Francis was the true Imitatio Christi, a poem compared to which the book of that name is merely prose.

Indeed, that is the charm about Christ, when all is said: he is just like a work of art. He does not really teach one anything, but by being brought into his presence one becomes something. And everybody is predestined to his presence. Once at least in his life each man walks with Christ to Emmaus.— *De Profundis.*

CLAPHAM JUNCTION

My lot has been one of public infamy, of long imprisonment, of misery, of ruin, of disgrace, but I am not worthy of it—not yet, at any rate. I remember that I used to say that I thought I could bear a real tragedy if it came to me with purple pall and a mask of noble sorrow, but that the dreadful thing about modernity was that it put tragedy into the raiment of comedy, so that the great realities seemed commonplace or grotesque or lacking in style. It is quite true about modernity. It has probably always been true about actual life. It is said that all martyrdoms seemed mean to the looker on. The nineteenth century is no exception to the rule.

188

Everything about my tragedy has been hideous, mean, repellent, lacking n style; our very dress makes us grotesque. We are the zanies of sorrow. We re clowns whose hearts are broken. We are specially designed to appeal o the sense of humour. On November 13th, 1895, I was brought down ere from London. From two o'clock till half-past two on that day I had o stand on the centre platform of Clapham Junction in convict dress, and andcuffed, for the world to look at. I had been taken out of the hospital vard without a moment's notice being given to me. Of all possible objects was the most grotesque. When people saw me they laughed. Each train s it came up swelled the audience. Nothing could exceed their amusement. hat was, of course, before they knew who I was. As soon as they had been nformed they laughed still more. For half an hour I stood there in the grey November rain surrounded by a jeering mob.—*De Profundis.*

THE BROKEN RESOLUTION

We call ours a utilitarian age, and we do not know the uses of any single hing. We have forgotten that water can cleanse, and fire purify, and that the Earth is mother to us all. As a consequence our art is of the moon and plays vith shadows, while Greek art is of the sun and deals directly with things. I eel sure that in elemental forces there is purification, and I want to go back o them and live in their presence.

Of course to one so modern as I am, 'Enfant de mon siècle,' merely to ook at the world will be always lovely. I tremble with pleasure when I think hat on the very day of my leaving prison both the laburnum and the lilac vill be blooming in the gardens, and that I shall see the wind stir into restless eauty the swaying gold of the one, and make the other toss the pale purple of ts plumes, so that all the air shall be Arabia for me. Linnæus fell on his knees nd wept for joy when he saw for the first time the long heath of some English pland made yellow with the tawny aromatic brooms of the common furze; nd I know that for me, to whom flowers are part of desire, there are tears vaiting in the petals of some rose. It has always been so with me from my oyhood. There is not a single colour hidden away in the chalice of a flower, r the curve of a shell, to which, by some subtle sympathy with the very soul f things, my nature does not answer. Like Gautier, I have always been one of those 'pour qui le monde visible existe.'

Still, I am conscious now that behind all this beauty, satisfying though i may be, there is some spirit hidden of which the painted forms and shapes ar but modes of manifestation, and it is with this spirit that I desire to become i harmony. I have grown tired of the articulate utterances of men and thing The Mystical in Art, the Mystical in Life, the Mystical in Nature this is what am looking for. It is absolutely necessary for me to find it somewhere.

All trials are trials for one's life, just as all sentences are sentences c death; and three times have I been tried. The first time I left the box to b arrested, the second time to be led back to the house of detention, the thir time to pass into a prison for two years. Society, as we have constituted it, wi have no place for me, has none to offer; but Nature, whose sweet rains fall o unjust and just alike, will have clefts in the rocks where I may hide, and secre valleys in whose silence I may weep undisturbed. She will hang the nigh with stars so that I may walk abroad in the darkness without stumbling, an send the wind over my footprints so that none may track me to my hurt: sh will cleanse me in great waters, and with bitter herbs make me whole.—*D Profundis.*

DOMESTICITY AT BERNEVAL

DIEPPE,

June 1st, 1897.

My Dear Robbie,—I propose to live at Berneval. I will not live in Paris nor in Algiers, nor in Southern Italy. Surely a house for a year, if I choose t continue there, at £32 is absurdly cheap. I could not live cheaper at a hotel You are penny foolish, and pound foolish—a dreadful state for my financie to be in. I told M. Bonnet that my bankers were MM. Ross et Cie, banquier célèbres de Londres—and now you suddenly show me that you have no plac among the great financial people, and are afraid of any investment over £31 10s. It is merely the extra ten shillings that baffles you. As regards peopl living on me, and the extra bedrooms: dear boy, there is no one who woul stay with me but you, and you will pay your own bill at the hotel for meals and as for your room, the charge will be nominally 2 francs 50 centimes night, but there will be lots of extras such as bougie, bain and hot water, and all cigarettes smoked in the bedrooms are charged extra. And if any one does not take the extras, of course he is charged more:—

Bain, 25 C.

Pas de bain, 50 C.

Cigarette dans la chambre à coucher, 10 C. pour chaque cigarette.

Pas de cigarette dans la chambre à coucher, 20 C. pour chaque cigarette.

This is the system at all good hotels. If Reggie comes, of course he will pay a little more: I cannot forget that he gave me a dressing-case. Sphinxes pay a hundred per cent more than any one else—they always did in Ancient Egypt.

But seriously, Robbie, if people stayed with me, of course they would pay their pension at the hotel. They would have to: except architects. A modern architect, like modern architecture, doesn't pay. But then I know only one architect and you are hiding him somewhere from me. I believe that he is as extinct as the dado, of which now only fossil remains are found, chiefly in the vicinity of Brompton, where they are sometimes discovered by workmen excavating. They are usually embedded in the old Lincrusta Walton strata, and are rare consequently.

I visited M. le Curé {4} to-day. He has a charming house and a jardin potager. He showed me over the church. To-morrow I sit in the choir by his special invitation. He showed me all his vestments. To-morrow he really will be charming in red. He knows I am a heretic, and believes Pusey is still alive. He says that God will convert England on account of England's kindness to les prêtres exilés at the time of the Revolution. It is to be the reward of that sea-lashed island.

Stained glass windows are wanted in the church; he has only six; fourteen more are needed. He gets them at 300 francs—£12—a window in Paris. I was nearly offering half a dozen, but remembered you, and so only gave him something *pour les pauvres*. You had a narrow escape, Robbie. You should be thankful.

I hope the £40 is on its way, and that the £60 will follow. I am going to hire a boat. It will save walking and so be an economy in the end. Dear Robbie, I must start well. If the life of St. Francis of Assissi awaits me I shall not be angry. Worse things might happen.

Yours,

OSCAR.

—*Letter to Robert Ross.*

A VISIT TO THE POPE

c/o COOK & SON, PIAZZA DI SPAGNA, ROME,

April 16th, 1900.

My dear Robbie,—I simply cannot write. It is too horrid, not of me but to me. It is a mode of paralysis—a cacoëthes tacendi—the one form that malady takes in me.

Well, all passed over very successfully. Palermo, where we stayed eight days, was lovely. The most beautifully situated town in the world—it dreams away its life in the concha d'oro, the exquisite valley that lies between two seas. The lemon groves and the orange gardens were so entirely perfect that I became quite a Pre-Raphaelite, and loathed the ordinary impressionists whose muddly souls and blurred intelligences would have rendered, but by mud and blur, those "golden lamps hung in a green night" that filled me with such joy. The elaborate and exquisite detail of the true Pre-Raphaelite is the compensation they offer us for the absence of motion; literature and motion being the only arts that are not immobile.

Then nowhere, not even at Ravenna, have I seen such mosaics as in the Capella Palatine, which from pavement to domed ceiling is all gold: one really feels as if one was sitting in the heart of a great honey-comb looking at angels singing: and looking at angels, or indeed at people, singing, is much nicer than listening to them, for this reason: the great artists always give to their angels lutes without strings, pipes without vent-holes, and reeds through which no wind can wander or make whistlings.

Monreale you have heard of—with its cloisters and cathedral: we often drove there.

I also made great friends with a young seminarist, who lived in the cathedral of Palermo—he and eleven others, in little rooms beneath the roof, like birds.

Every day he showed me all over the cathedral, I knelt before the huge porphyry sarcophagus in which Frederick the Second lies: it is a sublime bare monstrous thing—blood-coloured, and held up by lions who have caught some of the rage of the great Emperor's restless soul. At first my young friend, Giuseppe Loverdi, gave me information; but on the third day I gave information to him, and re-wrote history as usual, and told him all about the supreme King and his Court of Poets, and the terrible book that he never wrote. His reason for entering the church was singularly mediæval. I asked him why he thought of becoming a clerico, and how. He answered: "My father is a cook and most poor; and we are many at home, so it seemed to me a good thing that there should be in so small a house as ours, one mouth less to feed; for though I am slim, I eat much, too much, alas! I fear."

I told him to be comforted, because God used poverty often as a means of bringing people to Him, and used riches never, or rarely; so Giuseppe was comforted, and I gave him a little book of devotion, very pretty, and with far more pictures than prayers in it—so of great service to Giuseppe whose eyes are beautiful. I also gave him many lire, and prophesied for him a Cardinal's hat, if he remained very good and never forgot me.

At Naples we stopped three days: most of my friends are, as you know, in prison, but I met some of nice memory.

We came to Rome on Holy Thursday. H--- left on Saturday for Gland—and yesterday, to the terror of Grissell {5} and all the Papal Court, I appeared in the front rank of the pilgrims in the Vatican, and got the blessing of the Holy Father—a blessing they would have denied me.

He was wonderful as he was carried past me on his throne—not of flesh and blood, but a white soul robed in white and an artist as well as a saint—the only instance in history, if the newspapers are to be believed. I have seen nothing like the extraordinary grace of his gestures as he rose, from moment to moment, to bless—possibly the pilgrims, but certainly me.

Tree should see him. It is his only chance.

I was deeply impressed, and my walking-stick showed signs of budding, would have budded, indeed, only at the door of the Chapel it was taken from me by the Knave of Spades. This strange prohibition is, of course, in honour of Tannhäuser.

How did I get the ticket? By a miracle, of course. I thought it was hopeless and made no effort of any kind. On Saturday afternoon at five o'clock H--- and I went to have tea at the Hôtel de l'Europe. Suddenly, as I was eating buttered toast, a man—or what seemed to be one—dressed like a hotel porter entered and asked me would I like to see the Pope on Easter Day. I bowed my head humbly and said "Non sum dignus," or words to that effect. He at once produced a ticket!

When I tell you that his countenance was of supernatural ugliness, and that the price of the ticket was thirty pieces of silver, I need say no more.

An equally curious thing is that whenever I pass the hotel, which I do constantly, I see the same man. Scientists call that phenomenon an obsession of the visual nerve. You and I know better.

On the afternoon of Easter Day I heard Vespers at the Lateran: music quite lovely. At the close, a Bishop in red, and with red gloves—such as Pater talks of in Gaston de Latour—came out on the balcony and showed us the Relics. He was swarthy, and wore a yellow mitre. A sinister mediæval man, but superbly Gothic, just like the bishops carved on stalls or on portals: and when one thinks that once people mocked at stained-glass attitudes! they are the only attitudes for the clothes. The sight of the Bishop, whom I watched with fascination, filled me with the great sense of the realism of Gothic art. Neither in Greek art nor in Gothic art is there any pose. Posing was invented by bad portrait-painters; and the first person who posed was a stock-broker,

194

and he has gone on posing ever since.

I send you a photograph I took on Palm Sunday at Palermo. Do send me some of yours, and love me always, and try to read this letter.

Kindest regards to your dear mother.

Always,

OSCAR.

—*Letter to Robert Ross.*

FOOTNOTES

{1} "The Influence of Pater and Matthew Arnold in the Prose-Writing of Oscar Wilde," by Ernst Bendz. London: H. Grevel & Co., 1914.

{2} "The Eighteen Nineties: A Review of Art and Idea at the Close of the Nineteenth Century," by Holbrook Jackson. London: Grant Richards Ltd., 1913.

{3} Mortimer Menpes.

{4} M. Constant Trop-Hardy, died at Berneval, March 2, 1898.

{5} Hartwell de la Garde Grissell, a Papal Chamberlain.

SHORTER PROSE PIECES

PHRASES AND PHILOSOPHIES FOR THE USE OF THE YOUNG

(December 1894)

The first duty in life is to be as artificial as possible. What the second duty is no one has as yet discovered.

Wickedness is a myth invented by good people to account for the curious attractiveness of others.

If the poor only had profiles there would be no difficulty in solving the problem of poverty.

Those who see any difference between soul and body have neither.

A really well-made buttonhole is the only link between Art and

Nature.

Religions die when they are proved to be true. Science is the record of dead religions.

The well-bred contradict other people. The wise contradict themselves.

Nothing that actually occurs is of the smallest importance.

Dulness is the coming of age of seriousness.

In all unimportant matters, style, not sincerity, is the essential.

In all important matters, style, not sincerity, is the essential.

If one tells the truth one is sure, sooner or later, to be found out.

Pleasure is the only thing one should live for. Nothing ages like happiness.

It is only by not paying one's bills that one can hope to live in the memory of the commercial classes.

No crime is vulgar, but all vulgarity is crime. Vulgarity is the conduct of others.

Only the shallow know themselves.

Time is waste of money.

One should always be a little improbable.

There is a fatality about all good resolutions. They are invariably made too soon.

The only way to atone for being occasionally a little overdressed is by being always absolutely overeducated.

To be premature is to be perfect.

Any preoccupation with ideas of what is right or wrong in conduct shows an arrested intellectual development.

Ambition is the last refuge of the failure.

A truth ceases to be true when more than one person believes in it.

In examinations the foolish ask questions that the wise cannot answer.

Greek dress was in its essence inartistic. Nothing should reveal the body but the body.

One should either be a work of art, or wear a work of art.

It is only the superficial qualities that last. Man's deeper nature is soon found out.

Industry is the root of all ugliness.

The ages live in history through their anachronisms.

It is only the gods who taste of death. Apollo has passed away, but Hyacinth, whom men say he slew, lives on. Nero and Narcissus are always with us.

The old believe everything: the middle-aged suspect everything; the young know everything.

The condition of perfection is idleness: the aim of perfection is youth.

Only the great masters of style ever succeeded in being obscure.

There is something tragic about the enormous number of young men there are in England at the present moment who start life with perfect profiles, and end by adopting some useful profession.

To love oneself is the beginning of a life-long romance.

MRS. LANGTRY AS HESTER GRAZEBROOK

(*New York World*, November 7, 1882)

It is only in the best Greek gems, on the silver coins of Syracuse, or among the marble figures of the Parthenon frieze, that one can find the ideal representation of the marvellous beauty of that face which laughed through the leaves last night as Hester Grazebrook.

Pure Greek it is, with the grave low forehead, the exquisitely arched brow; the noble chiselling of the mouth, shaped as if it were the mouthpiece of an instrument of music; the supreme and splendid curve of the cheek; the augustly pillared throat which bears it all: it is Greek, because the lines which compose it are so definite and so strong, and yet so exquisitely harmonized that the effect is one of simple loveliness purely: Greek, because its essence and its quality, as is the quality of music and of architecture, is that of beauty based on absolutely mathematical laws.

But while art remains dumb and immobile in its passionless serenity with the beauty of this face it is different: the grey eyes lighten into blue or deepen into violet as fancy succeeds fancy; the lips become flower-like in laughter or, tremulous as a bird's wing, mould themselves at last into the strong and bitter moulds of pain or scorn. And then motion comes, and the statue wakes into life. But the life is not the ordinary life of common days: it is life with a new value given to it, the value of art: and the charm to me of Hester Grazebrook's acting in the first scene of the play last night was that mingling of classic grace with absolute reality which is the secret of all beautiful art, of the plastic work of the Greeks and of the pictures of Jean Francois Millet equally.

I do not think that the sovereignty and empire of women's beauty has at all passed away, though we may no longer go to war for them as the Greeks did for the daughter of Leda. The greatest empire still remains for them—the empire of art. And, indeed, this wonderful face, seen last night for the first time in America, has filled and permeated with the pervading image of its type the whole of our modern art in England. Last century it was the romantic type which dominated in art, the type loved by Reynolds and Gainsborough, of wonderful contrasts of colour, of exquisite and varying charm of expression, but without that definite plastic feeling which divides classic from romantic work. This type degenerated into mere facile prettiness in the hands of lesser masters, and, in protest against it, was created by the hands of the Pre-Raphaelites a new type, with its rare combination of Greek form with Florentine mysticism. But this mysticism becomes over- strained and a burden, rather than an aid to expression, and a desire for the pure Hellenic joy and serenity came in its place; and in all our modern work, in the paintings of such men as Albert Moore and Leighton and Whistler, we can trace the influence of this single face giving fresh life and inspiration in the form of a new artistic ideal.

SLAVES OF FASHION

Miss Leffler-Arnim's statement, in a lecture delivered recently at St. Saviour's Hospital, that "she had heard of instances where ladies were so determined not to exceed the fashionable measurement that they had actually held on to a cross-bar while their maids fastened the fifteen-inch corset," has excited a good deal of incredulity, but there is nothing really improbable in it. From the sixteenth century to our own day there is hardly any form of torture that has not been inflicted on girls, and endured by women, in obedience to the dictates of an unreasonable and monstrous Fashion. "In order to obtain a real Spanish figure," says Montaigne, "what a Gehenna of suffering will not women endure, drawn in and compressed by great coches entering the flesh; nay, sometimes they even die thereof!" "A few days after my arrival at school," Mrs. Somerville tells us in her memoirs, "although perfectly straight and well made, I was enclosed in stiff stays, with a steel busk in front; while above my frock, bands drew my shoulders back till the shoulder-blades met. Then a steel rod with a semi-circle, which went under my chin, was clasped to the steel busk in my stays. In this constrained state I and most of the younger girls had to prepare our lessons"; and in the life of Miss Edgeworth we read that, being sent to a certain fashionable establishment, "she underwent all the usual tortures of back- boards, iron collars and dumbs, and also (because she was a very tiny person) the unusual one of being hung by the neck to draw out the muscles and increase the growth," a signal failure in her case. Indeed, instances of absolute mutilation and misery are so common in the past that it is unnecessary to multiply them; but it is really sad to think that in our own day a civilized woman can hang on to a cross-bar while her maid laces her waist into a fifteen- inch circle. To begin with, the waist is not a circle at all, but an oval; nor can there be any greater error than to imagine that an unnaturally small waist gives an air of grace, or even of slightness, to the whole figure. Its effect, as a rule, is simply to exaggerate the width of the shoulders and the hips; and those whose figures possess that stateliness which is called stoutness by the vulgar, convert what is a quality into a defect by yielding to the silly edicts of Fashion on the subject of tight-lacing. The shionable English waist, also, is not merely far too small, and consequently uite out of proportion to the rest of the figure, but it is worn far too low own. I use the expression "worn" advisedly, for a waist nowadays seems to e regarded as an article of apparel to be put on when and where one likes. A ng waist always implies shortness of the lower limbs, and, from the artistic oint of view, has the effect of diminishing the height; and I am glad to see at many of the most charming women in Paris are returning to the idea of e Directoire style of dress. This style is not by any means perfect, but at least has the merit of indicating the proper position of the waist. I feel quite sure at all English women of culture and position will set their faces against such upid and dangerous practices as are related by Miss Leffler-Arnim. Fashion's otto is: Il faut souffrir pour etre belle; but the motto of art and of common-nse is: Il faut etre bete pour souffrir.

Talking of Fashion, a critic in the Pall Mall Gazelle expresses his surprise at I should have allowed an illustration of a hat, covered with "the bodies f dead birds," to appear in the first number of the Woman's World; and s I have received many letters on the subject, it is only right that I should ate my exact position in the matter. Fashion is such an essential part of e mundus muliebris of our day, that it seems to me absolutely necessary at its growth, development, and phases should be duly chronicled; and e historical and practical value of such a record depends entirely upon its erfect fidelity to fact. Besides, it is quite easy for the children of light to adapt most any fashionable form of dress to the requirements of utility and the emands of good taste. The Sarah Bernhardt tea-gown, for instance, figured the present issue, has many good points about it, and the gigantic dress-mprover does not appear to me to be really essential to the mode; and though e Postillion costume of the fancy dress ball is absolutely detestable in its lliness and vulgarity, the so-called Late Georgian costume in the same plate rather pleasing. I must, however, protest against the idea that to chronicle e development of Fashion implies any approval of the particular forms that ashion may adopt.

WOMAN'S DRESS

(*Pall Mall Gazette*, October 14, 1884)

Mr. Oscar Wilde, who asks us to permit him 'that most charming of all pleasures, the pleasure of answering one's critics,' sends us the following remarks:—

The "Girl Graduate" must of course have precedence, not merely for her sex but for her sanity: her letter is extremely sensible. She makes two points: that high heels are a necessity for any lady who wishes to keep her dress clean from the Stygian mud of our streets, and that without a tight corset the ordinary number of petticoats and etceteras' cannot be properly or conveniently held up. Now, it is quite true that as long as the lower garments are suspended from the hips a corset is an absolute necessity; the mistake lies in not suspending all apparel from the shoulders. In the latter case a corset becomes useless, the body is left free and unconfined for respiration and motion, there is more health, and consequently more beauty. Indeed all the most ungainly and uncomfortable articles of dress that fashion has ever in her folly prescribed, not the tight corset merely, but the farthingale, the vertugadin, the hoop, the crinoline, and that modern monstrosity the so-called "dress improver" also, all of them have owed their origin to the same error, the error of not seeing that it is from the shoulders, and from the shoulders only, that all garments should be hung.

And as regards high heels, I quite admit that some additional height to the shoe or boot is necessary if long gowns are to be worn in the street; but what I object to is that the height should be given to the heel only, and not to the sole of the foot also. The modern high-heeled boot is, in fact, merely the clog of the time of Henry VI., with the front prop left out, and its inevitable effect is to throw the body forward, to shorten the steps, and consequently to produce that want of grace which always follows want of freedom.

Why should clogs be despised? Much art has been expended on clogs. They have been made of lovely woods, and delicately inlaid with ivory, and with mother-of-pearl. A clog might be a dream of beauty, and, if not too high or too heavy, most comfortable also. But if there be any who do not like clogs, let them try some adaptation of the trouser of the Turkish lady, which is loose round the limb and tight at the ankle.

The "Girl Graduate," with a pathos to which I am not insensible, entreats me not to apotheosize "that awful, befringed, beflounced, and bekilted divided skirt." Well, I will acknowledge that the fringes, the flounces, and the kilting do certainly defeat the whole object of the dress, which is that of ease and liberty; but I regard these things as mere wicked superfluities, tragic proofs that the divided skirt is ashamed of its own division. The principle of the dress is good, and, though it is not by any means perfection, it is a step towards it.

Here I leave the "Girl Graduate," with much regret, for Mr. Wentworth Huyshe. Mr. Huyshe makes the old criticism that Greek dress is unsuited to our climate, and, to me the somewhat new assertion, that the men's dress of a hundred years ago was preferable to that of the second part of the seventeenth century, which I consider to have been the exquisite period of English costume.

Now, as regards the first of these two statements, I will say, to begin with, that the warmth of apparel does not depend really on the number of garments worn, but on the material of which they are made. One of the chief faults of modern dress is that it is composed of far too many articles of clothing, most of which are of the wrong substance; but over a substratum of pure wool, such as is supplied by Dr. Jaeger under the modern German system, some modification of Greek costume is perfectly applicable to our climate, our country and our century. This important fact has already been pointed out by Mr. E. W. Godwin in his excellent, though too brief handbook on Dress, contributed to the Health Exhibition. I call it an important fact because it makes almost any form of lovely costume perfectly practicable in our cold climate. Mr. Godwin, it is true, points out that the English ladies of the thirteenth century abandoned after some time the flowing garments of the early Renaissance in favour of a tighter mode, such as Northern Europe seems to demand. This I quite admit, and its significance; but what I contend, and what I am sure Mr. Godwin would agree with me in, is that the principles the laws of Greek dress may be perfectly realized, even in a moderately tight gown with sleeves: I mean the principle of suspending all apparel from the shoulders, and of relying for beauty of effect not on the stiff ready-made ornaments of the modern milliner—the bows where there should be no bows and the flounces where there should be no flounces—but on the exquisite play of light and line that one gets from rich and rippling folds. I am not proposing any antiquarian revival of an ancient costume, but trying merely to point out the right laws of dress, laws which are dictated by art and not by archaeology, by science and not by fashion; and just as the best work of art in our days is that which combines classic grace with absolute reality, so from a continuation of the Greek principles of beauty with the German principles of health will come, I feel certain, the costume of the future.

And now to the question of men's dress, or rather to Mr. Huyshe's claim of the superiority, in point of costume, of the last quarter of the eighteenth century over the second quarter of the seventeenth. The broad-brimmed hat of 1640 kept the rain of winter and the glare of summer from the face; the same cannot be said of the hat of one hundred years ago, which, with its comparatively narrow brim and high crown, was the precursor of the modern "chimney-pot": a wide turned-down collar is a healthier thing than a strangling stock, and a short cloak much more comfortable than a sleeved overcoat, even though the latter may have had "three capes"; a cloak is easier to put on and off, lies lightly on the shoulder in summer, and wrapped round one in winter keeps one perfectly warm. A doublet, again, is simpler than a coat and waistcoat; instead of two garments one has one; by not being open also it protects the chest better.

Short loose trousers are in every way to be preferred to the tight knee-breeches which often impede the proper circulation of the blood; and finally, the soft leather boots which could be worn above or below the knee, are more supple, and give consequently more freedom, than the stiff Hessian which Mr. Huyshe so praises. I say nothing about the question of grace and picturesqueness, for I suppose that no one, not even Mr. Huyshe, would prefer a maccaroni to a cavalier, a Lawrence to a Vandyke, or the third George to the first Charles; but for ease, warmth and comfort this seventeenth-century dress is infinitely superior to anything that came after it, and I do not think it is excelled by any preceding form of costume. I sincerely trust that we may soon see in England some national revival of it.

MORE RADICAL IDEAS UPON DRESS REFORM

(*Pall Mall Gazette*, November 11, 1884)

I have been much interested at reading the large amount of correspondence that has been called forth by my recent lecture on Dress. It shows me that the subject of dress reform is one that is occupying many wise and charming people, who have at heart the principles of health, freedom, and beauty in costume, and I hope that "H. B. T." and "Materfamilias" will have all the real influence which their letters—excellent letters both of them— certainly deserve.

I turn first to Mr. Huyshe's second letter, and the drawing that accompanies it; but before entering into any examination of the theory contained in each, I think I should state at once that I have absolutely no idea whether this gentleman wears his hair long or short, or his cuffs back or forward, or indeed what he is like at all. I hope he consults his own comfort and wishes in everything which has to do with his dress, and is allowed to enjoy that individualism in apparel which he so eloquently claims for himself, and so foolishly tries to deny to others; but I really could not take Mr. Wentworth Huyshe's personal appearance as any intellectual basis for an investigation of the principles which should guide the costume of a nation. I am not denying the force, or even the popularity, of the "'Eave arf a brick" school of criticism, but I acknowledge it does not interest me. The gamin in the gutter may be a necessity, but the gamin in discussion is a nuisance. So I will proceed at once to the real point at issue, the value of the late eighteenth-century costume over that worn in the second quarter of the seventeenth: the relative merits, that is, of the principles contained in each. Now, as regards the eighteenth-century costume, Mr. Wentworth Huyshe acknowledges that he has had no practical experience of it at all; in fact he makes a pathetic appeal to his friends to corroborate him in his assertion, which I do not question for a moment, that he has never been "guilty of the eccentricity" of wearing himself the dress which he proposes for general adoption by others. There is something so naive and so amusing about this last passage in Mr. Huyshe's etter that I am really in doubt whether I am not doing him a wrong in egarding him as having any serious, or sincere, views on the question of a ossible reform in dress; still, as irrespective of any attitude of Mr. Huyshe's n the matter, the subject is in itself an interesting one, I think it is worth ontinuing, particularly as I have myself worn this late eighteenth-century Iress many times, both in public and in private, and so may claim to have a ery positive right to speak on its comfort and suitability. The particular form f the dress I wore was very similar to that given in Mr. Godwin's handbook, rom a print of Northcote's, and had a certain elegance and grace about it which was very charming; still, I gave it up for these reasons:- After a further onsideration of the laws of dress I saw that a doublet is a far simpler and asier garment than a coat and waistcoat, and, if buttoned from the shoulder, ar warmer also, and that tails have no place in costume, except on some Darwinian theory of heredity; from absolute experience in the matter I found hat the excessive tightness of knee-breeches is not really comfortable if one years them constantly; and, in fact, I satisfied myself that the dress is not ne founded on any real principles. The broad-brimmed hat and loose cloak, which, as my object was not, of course, historical accuracy but modern ease, I ad always worn with the costume in question, I have still retained, and find hem most comfortable.

Well, although Mr. Huyshe has no real experience of the dress he roposes, he gives us a drawing of it, which he labels, somewhat prematurely, An ideal dress." An ideal dress of course it is not; "passably picturesque," he ays I may possibly think it; well, passably picturesque it may be, but not eautiful, certainly, simply because it is not founded on right principles, or, ndeed, on any principles at all. Picturesqueness one may get in a variety f ways; ugly things that are strange, or unfamiliar to us, for instance, may e picturesque, such as a late sixteenth-century costume, or a Georgian ouse. Ruins, again, may be picturesque, but beautiful they never can be, ecause their lines are meaningless. Beauty, in fact, is to be got only from the erfection of principles; and in "the ideal dress" of Mr. Huyshe there are no deas or principles at all, much less the perfection of either. Let us examine t, and see its faults; they are obvious to any one who desires more than a Fancy-dress ball" basis for costume. To begin with, the hat and boots are all wrong. Whatever one wears on the extremities, such as the feet and head, should, for the sake of comfort, be made of a soft material, and for the sake of freedom should take its shape from the way one chooses to wear it, and not from any stiff, stereotyped design of hat or boot maker. In a hat made on right principles one should be able to turn the brim up or down according as the day is dark or fair, dry or wet; but the hat brim of Mr. Huyshe's drawing is perfectly stiff, and does not give much protection to the face, or the possibility of any at all to the back of the head or the ears, in case of a cold east wind; whereas the bycocket, a hat made in accordance with the right laws, can be turned down behind and at the sides, and so give the same warmth as a hood. The crown, again, of Mr. Huyshe's hat is far too high; a high crown diminishes the stature of a small person, and in the case of any one who is tall is a great inconvenience when one is getting in and out of hansoms and railway carriages, or passing under a street awning: in no case is it of any value whatsoever, and being useless it is of course against the principles of dress.

As regards the boots, they are not quite so ugly or so uncomfortable as the hat; still they are evidently made of stiff leather, as otherwise they would fall down to the ankle, whereas the boot should be made of soft leather always, and if worn high at all must be either laced up the front or carried well over the knee: in the latter case one combines perfect freedom for walking together with perfect protection against rain, neither of which advantages a short stiff boot will ever give one, and when one is resting in the house the long soft boot can be turned down as the boot of 1640 was. Then there is the overcoat: now, what are the right principles of an overcoat? To begin with, it should be capable of being easily put on or off, and worn over any kind of dress; consequently it should never have narrow sleeves, such as are shown in Mr. Huyshe's drawing. If an opening or slit for the arm is required it should be made quite wide, and may be protected by a flap, as in that excellent overall the modern Inverness cape; secondly, it should not be too tight, as otherwise all freedom of walking is impeded. If the young gentleman in the drawing buttons his overcoat he may succeed in being statuesque, though that I doubt very strongly, but he will never succeed in being swift; his super-totus is made for him on no principle whatsoever; a super- totus, or overall, should be capable of being worn long or short, quite loose or moderately tight, just as the wearer wishes; he should be able to have one arm free and one arm covered or both arms free or both arms covered, just as he chooses for his convenience in riding, walking, or driving; an overall again should never be heavy, and should always be warm: lastly, it should be capable of being easily carried if one wants to take it off; in fact, its principles are those of freedom and comfort, and a cloak realizes them all, just as much as an overcoat of the pattern suggested by Mr. Huyshe violates them.

The knee-breeches are of course far too tight; any one who has worn them for any length of time—any one, in fact, whose views on the subject are not purely theoretical—will agree with me there; like everything else in the dress, they are a great mistake. The substitution of the jacket for the coat and waistcoat of the period is a step in the right direction, which I am glad to see; it is, however, far too tight over the hips for any possible comfort. Whenever a jacket or doublet comes below the waist it should be slit at each side. In the seventeenth century the skirt of the jacket was sometimes laced on by points and tags, so that it could be removed at will, sometimes it was merely left open at the sides: in each case it exemplified what are always the true principles of dress, I mean freedom and adaptability to circumstances.

Finally, as regards drawings of this kind, I would point out that there is absolutely no limit at all to the amount of "passably picturesque" costumes which can be either revived or invented for us; but that unless a costume is founded on principles and exemplified laws, it never can be of any real value to us in the reform of dress. This particular drawing of Mr. Huyshe's, for instance, proves absolutely nothing, except that our grandfathers did not understand the proper laws of dress. There is not a single rule of right costume which is not violated in it, for it gives us stiffness, tightness and discomfort instead of comfort, freedom and ease.

Now here, on the other hand, is a dress which, being founded on principles, can serve us as an excellent guide and model; it has been drawn for me, most kindly, by Mr. Godwin from the Duke of Newcastle's delightful book on horsemanship, a book which is one of our best authorities on our best era of costume. I do not of course propose it necessarily for absolute imitation; that is not the way in which one should regard it; it is not, I mean, a revival of a dead costume, but a realization of living laws. I give it as an example of a particular application of principles which are universally right. This rationally dressed young man can turn his hat brim down if it rains, and his loose trousers and boots down if he is tired—that is, he can adapt his costume to circumstances; then he enjoys perfect freedom, the arms and legs are not made awkward or uncomfortable by the excessive tightness of narrow sleeves and knee-breeches, and the hips are left quite untrammelled, always an important point; and as regards comfort, his jacket is not too loose for warmth, nor too close for respiration; his neck is well protected without being strangled, and even his ostrich feathers, if any Philistine should object to them, are not merely dandyism, but fan him very pleasantly, I am sure, in summer, and when the weather is bad they are no doubt left at home, and his cloak taken out. THE VALUE OF THE DRESS IS SIMPLY THAT EVERY SEPARATE ARTICLE OF IT EXPRESSES A LAW. My young man is consequently apparelled with ideas, while Mr. Huyshe's young man is stiffened with facts; the latter teaches one nothing; from the former one learns everything. I need hardly say that this dress is good, not because it is seventeenth century, but because it is constructed on the true principles of costume, just as a square lintel or pointed arch is good, not because one may be Greek and the other Gothic, but because each of them is the best method of spanning a certain-sized opening, or resisting a certain weight. The fact, however, that this dress was generally worn in England two centuries and a half ago shows at least this, that the right laws of dress have been understood and realized in our country, and so in our country may be realized and understood again. As regards the absolute beauty of this dress and its meaning, I should like to say a few words more. Mr. Wentworth Huyshe solemnly announces that "he and those who think with him" cannot permit this question of beauty to be imported into the question of dress; that he and those who think with him take "practical views on the subject," and so on. Well, I will not enter here into a discussion as to how far any one who does not take beauty and the value of beauty into account can claim to be practical at all. The word practical is nearly always the last refuge of the uncivilized. Of all misused words it is the most evilly treated. But what I want to point out is that beauty is essentially organic; that is, it comes, not from without, but from within, not from any added prettiness, but from the perfection of its own being; and that consequently, as the body is beautiful, so all apparel that rightly clothes it must be beautiful also in its construction and in its lines.

I have no more desire to define ugliness than I have daring to define beauty; but still I would like to remind those who mock at beauty as being an unpractical thing of this fact, that an ugly thing is merely a thing that is badly made, or a thing that does not serve it purpose; that ugliness is want of fitness; that ugliness is failure; that ugliness is uselessness, such as ornament in the wrong place, while beauty, as some one finely said, is the purgation of all superfluities. There is a divine economy about beauty; it gives us just what is needful and no more, whereas ugliness is always extravagant; ugliness is a spendthrift and wastes its material; in fine, ugliness—and I would commend this remark to Mr. Wentworth Huyshe—ugliness, as much in costume as in anything else, is always the sign that somebody has been unpractical. So the costume of the future in England, if it is founded on the true laws of freedom, comfort, and adaptability to circumstances, cannot fail to be most beautiful also, because beauty is the sign always of the rightness of principles, the mystical seal that is set upon what is perfect, and upon what is perfect only.

As for your other correspondent, the first principle of dress that all garments should be hung from the shoulders and not from the waist seems to me to be generally approved of, although an "Old Sailor" declares that no sailors or athletes ever suspend their clothes from the shoulders, but always from the hips. My own recollection of the river and running ground at Oxford—those two homes of Hellenism in our little Gothic town—is that the best runners and rowers (and my own college turned out many) wore always a tight jersey, with short drawers attached to it, the whole costume being woven in one piece. As for sailors, it is true, I admit, and the bad custom seems to involve that constant "hitching up" of the lower garments which, however popular in transpontine dramas, cannot, I think, but be considered an extremely awkward habit; and as all awkwardness comes from discomfort of some kind, I trust that this point in our sailor's dress will be looked to in the coming reform of our navy, for, in spite of all protests, I hope we are about to reform everything, from torpedoes to top-hats, and from crinolettes to cruises.

Then as regards clogs, my suggestion of them seems to have aroused a great deal of terror. Fashion in her high-heeled boots has screamed, and the dreadful word "anachronism" has been used. Now, whatever is useful cannot be an anachronism. Such a word is applicable only to the revival of some folly; and, besides, in the England of our own day clogs are still worn in many of our manufacturing towns, such as Oldham. I fear that in Oldham they may not be dreams of beauty; in Oldham the art of inlaying them with ivory and with pearl may possibly be unknown; yet in Oldham they serve their purpose. Nor is it so long since they were worn by the upper classes of this country generally. Only a few days ago I had the pleasure of talking to a lady who remembered with affectionate regret the clogs of her girlhood; they were, according to her, not too high nor too heavy, and were provided, besides, with some kind of spring in the sole so as to make them the more supple for the foot in walking. Personally, I object to all additional height being given to a boot or shoe; it is really against the proper principles of dress, although, if any such height is to be given it should be by means of two props; not one; but what I should prefer to see is some adaptation of the divided skirt or long and moderately loose knickerbockers. If, however, the divided skirt is to be of any positive value, it must give up all idea of "being identical in appearance with an ordinary skirt"; it must diminish the moderate width of each of its divisions, and sacrifice its foolish frills and flounces; the moment it imitates a dress it is lost; but let it visibly announce itself as what it actually is, and it will go far towards solving a real difficulty. I feel sure that there will be found many graceful and charming girls ready to adopt a costume founded on these principles, in spite of Mr. Wentworth Huyshe's terrible threat that he will not propose to them as long as they wear it, for all charges of a want of womanly character in these forms of dress are really meaningless; every right article of apparel belongs equally to both sexes, and there is absolutely no such thing as a definitely feminine garment. One word of warning I should like to be allowed to give: The over-tunic should be made full and moderately loose; it may, if desired, be shaped more or less to the figure, but in no case should it be confined at the waist by any straight band or belt; on the contrary, it should fall from the shoulder to the knee, or below it, in fine curves and vertical

218

lines, giving more freedom and consequently more grace. Few garments are so absolutely unbecoming as a belted tunic that reaches to the knees, a fact which I wish some of our Rosalinds would consider when they don doublet and hose; indeed, to the disregard of this artistic principle is due the ugliness, the want of proportion, in the Bloomer costume, a costume which in other respects is sensible.

COSTUME

Are we not all weary of him, that venerable impostor fresh from the steps of the Piazza di Spagna, who, in the leisure moments that he can spare from his customary organ, makes the round of the studios and is waited for in Holland Park? Do we not all recognize him, when, with the gay insouciance of his nation, he reappears on the walls of our summer exhibitions as everything that he is not, and as nothing that he is, glaring at us here as a patriarch of Canaan, here beaming as a brigand from the Abruzzi? Popular is he, this poor peripatetic professor of posing, with those whose joy it is to paint the posthumous portrait of the last philanthropist who in his lifetime had neglected to be photographed,—yet he is the sign of the decadence, the symbol of decay.

For all costumes are caricatures. The basis of Art is not the Fancy Ball. Where there is loveliness of dress, there is no dressing up. And so, were our national attire delightful in colour, and in construction simple and sincere; were dress the expression of the loveliness that it shields and of the swiftness and motion that it does not impede; did its lines break from the shoulder instead of bulging from the waist; did the inverted wineglass cease to be the ideal of form; were these things brought about, as brought about they will be, then would painting be no longer an artificial reaction against the ugliness of life, but become, as it should be, the natural expression of life's beauty. Nor would painting merely, but all the other arts also, be the gainers by a change such as that which I propose; the gainers, I mean, through the increased atmosphere of Beauty by which the artists would be surrounded and in which they would grow up. For Art is not to be taught in Academies. It is what one looks at, not what one listens to, that makes the artist. The real schools should be the streets. There is not, for instance, a single delicate line, or delightful proportion, in the dress of the Greeks, which is not echoed exquisitely in their architecture. A nation arrayed in stove-pipe hats and dress-improvers might have built the Pantechnicon possibly, but the Parthenon never. And finally, there is this to be said: Art, it is true, can never have any other claim but her own perfection, and it may be that the artist, desiring merely to contemplate and to create, is wise in not busying himself about change in others: yet wisdom is not always the best; there are times when she sinks to the level of common-sense; and from the passionate folly of those—and there are many—who desire that Beauty shall be confined no longer to the bric-a-brac of the collector and the dust of the museum, but shall be, as it should be, the natural and national inheritance of all,— from this noble unwisdom, I say, who knows what new loveliness shall be given to life, and, under these more exquisite conditions, what perfect artist born? Le milieu se renouvelant, l'art se renouvelle.

THE AMERICAN INVASION

(March 1887)

A terrible danger is hanging over the Americans in London. Their future and their reputation this season depend entirely on the success of Buffalo Bill and Mrs. Brown-Potter. The former is certain to draw; for English people are far more interested in American barbarism than they are in American civilization. When they sight Sandy Hook they look to their rifles and ammunition; and, after dining once at Delmonico's, start off for Colorado or California, for Montana or the Yellow Stone Park. Rocky Mountains charm them more than riotous millionaires; they have been known to prefer buffaloes to Boston. Why should they not? The cities of America are inexpressibly tedious. The Bostonians take their learning too sadly; culture with them is an accomplishment rather than an atmosphere; their "Hub," as they call it, is the paradise of prigs. Chicago is a sort of monster-shop, full of bustle and bores. Political life at Washington is like political life in a suburban vestry. Baltimore is amusing for a week, but Philadelphia is dreadfully provincial; and though one can dine in New York one could not dwell there. Better the Far West with its grizzly bears and its untamed cowboys, its free open-air life and its free open- air manners, its boundless prairie and its boundless mendacity! This is what Buffalo Bill is going to bring to London; and we have no doubt that London will fully appreciate his show.

With regard to Mrs. Brown-Potter, as acting is no longer considered absolutely essential for success on the English stage, there is really no reason why the pretty bright-eyed lady who charmed us all last June by her merry laugh and her nonchalant ways, should not— to borrow an expression from her native language—make a big boom and paint the town red. We sincerely hope she will; for, on the whole, the American invasion has done English society a great deal of good. American women are bright, clever, and wonderfully cosmopolitan. Their patriotic feelings are limited to an admiration for Niagara and a regret for the Elevated Railway; and, unlike the men, they never bore us with Bunkers Hill. They take their dresses from Paris and their manners from Piccadilly, and wear both charmingly. They have a quaint pertness, a delightful conceit, a native self-assertion. They insist on being paid compliments and have almost succeeded in making Englishmen eloquent. For our aristocracy they have an ardent admiration; they adore titles and are a permanent blow to Republican principles. In the art of amusing men they are adepts, both by nature and education, and can actually tell a story without forgetting the point—an accomplishment that is extremely rare among the women of other countries. It is true that they lack repose and that their voices are somewhat harsh and strident when they land first at Liverpool; but after a time one gets to love those pretty whirlwinds in petticoats that sweep so recklessly through society and are so agitating to all duchesses who have daughters. There is something fascinating in their funny, exaggerated gestures and their petulant way of tossing the head. Their eyes have no magic nor mystery in them, but they challenge us for combat; and when we engage we are always worsted. Their lips seem made for laughter and yet they never grimace. As for their voices they soon get them into tune. Some of them have been known to acquire a fashionable drawl in two seasons; and after they have been presented to Royalty they all roll their R's as vigorously as a young equerry or an old lady-in-waiting. Still, they never really lose their accent; it keeps peeping out here and there, and when they chatter together they are like a bevy of peacocks. Nothing is more amusing than to watch two American girls greeting each other in a drawing-room or in the Row. They are like children with their shrill staccato cries of wonder, their odd little exclamations. Their conversation sounds like a series of exploding crackers; they are exquisitely incoherent and use a sort of primitive, emotional language. After five minutes they are left beautifully breathless and look at each other half in amusement and half in affection. If a stolid young Englishman is fortunate enough to be introduced to them he is amazed at their extraordinary vivacity, their electric quickness of repartee, their inexhaustible store of curious catchwords. He never really understands them, for their thoughts flutter about with the sweet irresponsibility of butterflies; but he is pleased and amused and feels as if he were in an aviary. On the whole, American girls have a wonderful charm and, perhaps, the chief secret of their charm is that they never talk seriously except about amusements. They have, however, one grave fault—their mothers.

Dreary as were those old Pilgrim Fathers who left our shores more than two centuries ago to found a New England beyond the seas, the Pilgrim Mothers who have returned to us in the nineteenth century are drearier still.

Here and there, of course, there are exceptions, but as a class they are either dull, dowdy or dyspeptic. It is only fair to the rising generation of America to state that they are not to blame for this. Indeed, they spare no pains at all to bring up their parents properly and to give them a suitable, if somewhat late, education. From its earliest years every American child spends most of its time in correcting the faults of its father and mother; and no one who has had the opportunity of watching an American family on the deck of an Atlantic steamer, or in the refined seclusion of a New York boarding-house, can fail to have been struck by this characteristic of their civilization. In America the young are always ready to give to those who are older than themselves the full benefits of their inexperience. A boy of only eleven or twelve years of age will firmly but kindly point out to his father his defects of manner or temper; will never weary of warning him against extravagance, idleness, late hours, unpunctuality, and the other temptations to which the aged are so particularly exposed; and sometimes, should he fancy that he is monopolizing too much of the conversation at dinner, will remind him, across the table, of the new child's adage, "Parents should be seen, not heard." Nor does any mistaken idea of kindness prevent the little American girl from censuring her mother whenever it is necessary. Often, indeed, feeling that a rebuke conveyed in the presence of others is more truly efficacious than one merely whispered in the quiet of the nursery, she will call the attention of perfect strangers to her mother's general untidiness, her want of intellectual Boston conversation, immoderate love of iced water and green corn, stinginess in the matter of candy, ignorance of the usages of the best Baltimore Society, bodily ailments, and the like. In fact, it may be truly said that no American child is ever blind to the deficiencies of its parents, no matter how much it may love them.

Yet, somehow, this educational system has not been so successful as it deserved. In many cases, no doubt, the material with which the children had to deal was crude and incapable of real development; but the fact remains that the American mother is a tedious person. The American father is better, for he is never seen in London. He passes his life entirely in Wall Street and communicates with his family once a month by means of a telegram in cipher. The mother, however, is always with us, and, lacking the quick imitative faculty of the younger generation, remains uninteresting and provincial to the last. In spite of her, however, the American girl is always welcome. She brightens our dull dinner parties for us and makes life go pleasantly by for a season. In the race for coronets she often carries off the prize; but, once she has gained the victory, she is generous and forgives her English rivals everything, even their beauty.

Warned by the example of her mother that American women do not grow old gracefully, she tries not to grow old at all and often succeeds. She has exquisite feet and hands, is always bien chaussee et bien gantee and can talk brilliantly upon any subject, provided that she knows nothing about it.

Her sense of humour keeps her from the tragedy of a grande passion, and, as there is neither romance nor humility in her love, she makes an excellent wife. What her ultimate influence on English life will be it is difficult to estimate at present; but there can be no doubt that, of all the factors that have contributed to the social revolution of London, there are few more important, and none more delightful, than the American Invasion.

SERMONS IN STONES AT BLOOMSBURY THE NEW SCULPTURE ROOM AT THE BRITISH MUSEUM

(October 1887)

Through the exertions of Sir Charles Newton, to whom every student o classic art should be grateful, some of the wonderful treasures so long immure in the grimy vaults of the British Museum have at last been brought to light and the new Sculpture Room now opened to the public will amply repay th trouble of a visit, even from those to whom art is a stumbling-block and rock of offence. For setting aside the mere beauty of form, outline and mass the grace and loveliness of design and the delicacy of technical treatment here we have shown to us what the Greeks and Romans thought about death and the philosopher, the preacher, the practical man of the world, and eve the Philistine himself, cannot fail to be touched by these "sermons in stones, with their deep significance, their fertile suggestion, their plain humanity Common tombstones they are, most of them, the work not of famous artist but of simple handicraftsmen, only they were wrought in days when ever handicraft was an art. The finest specimens, from the purely artistic poin of view, are undoubtedly the two stelai found at Athens. They are both th tombstones of young Greek athletes. In one the athlete is represented handin; his strigil to his slave, in the other the athlete stands alone, strigil in hand They do not belong to the greatest period of Greek art, they have not the grand style of the Phidian age, but they are beautiful for all that, and it is impossibl not to be fascinated by their exquisite grace and by the treatment which is s simple in its means, so subtle in its effect. All the tombstones, however, ar full of interest. Here is one of two ladies of Smyrna who were so remarkabl in their day that the city voted them honorary crowns; here is a Greek docto examining a little boy who is suffering from indigestion; here is the memoria of Xanthippus who, probably, was a martyr to gout, as he is holding in hi hand the model of a foot, intended, no doubt, as a votive offering to som god. A lovely stele from Rhodes gives us a family group. The husband is o horseback and is bidding farewell to his wife, who seems as if she woul follow him but is being held back by a little child. The pathos of parting from those we love is the central motive of Greek funeral art. It is repeated in every possible form, and each mute marble stone seems to murmur [Greek text]. Roman art is different. It introduces vigorous and realistic portraiture and deals with pure family life far more frequently than Greek art does. They are very ugly, those stern-looking Roman men and women whose portraits are exhibited on their tombs, but they seem to have been loved and respected by their children and their servants. Here is the monument of Aphrodisius and Atilia, a Roman gentleman and his wife, who died in Britain many centuries ago, and whose tombstone was found in the Thames; and close by it stands a stele from Rome with the busts of an old married couple who are certainly marvellously ill-favoured. The contrast between the abstract Greek treatment of the idea of death and the Roman concrete realization of the individuals who have died is extremely curious.

Besides the tombstones, the new Sculpture Room contains some most fascinating examples of Roman decorative art under the Emperors. The most wonderful of all, and this alone is worth a trip to Bloomsbury, is a bas-relief representing a marriage scene, Juno Pronuba is joining the hands of a handsome young noble and a very stately lady. There is all the grace of Perugino in this marble, all the grace of Raphael even. The date of it is uncertain, but the particular cut of the bridegroom's beard seems to point to the time of the Emperor Hadrian. It is clearly the work of Greek artists and is one of the most beautiful bas-reliefs in the whole Museum. There is something in it which reminds one of the music and the sweetness of Propertian verse. Then we have delightful friezes of children. One representing children playing on musical instruments might have suggested much of the plastic art of Florence. Indeed, as we view these marbles it is not difficult to see whence the Renaissance sprang and to what we owe the various forms of Renaissance art. The frieze of the Muses, each of whom wears in her hair a feather plucked from the wings of the vanquished sirens, is extremely fine; there is a lovely little bas-relief of two cupids racing in chariots; and the frieze of recumbent Amazons has some splendid qualities of design. A frieze of children playing with the armour of the god Mars should also be mentioned. It is full of fancy and delicate humour.

We hope that some more of the hidden treasures will shortly be catalogued and shown. In the vaults at present there is a very remarkable bas-relief of the marriage of Cupid and Psyche, and another representing the professional mourners weeping over the body of the dead. The fine cast of the Lion of Chaeronea should also be brought up, and so should the stele with the marvellous portrait of the Roman slave. Economy is an excellent public virtue, but the parsimony that allows valuable works of art to remain in the grim and gloom of a damp cellar is little short of a detestable public vice.

L'ENVOI

Amongst the many young men in England who are seeking along with me to continue and to perfect the English Renaissance—jeunes guerriers du drapeau romantique, as Gautier would have called us— there is none whose love of art is more flawless and fervent, whose artistic sense of beauty is more subtle and more delicate—none, indeed, who is dearer to myself—than the young poet whose verses I have brought with me to America; verses full of sweet sadness, and yet full of joy; for the most joyous poet is not he who sows the desolate highways of this world with the barren seed of laughter, but he who makes his sorrow most musical, this indeed being the meaning of joy in art—that incommunicable element of artistic delight which, in poetry, for instance, comes from what Keats called "sensuous life of verse," the element of song in the singing, made so pleasurable to us by that wonder of motion which often has its origin in mere musical impulse, and in painting is to be sought for, from the subject never, but from the pictorial charm only—the scheme and symphony of the colour, the satisfying beauty of the design: so that the ultimate expression of our artistic movement in painting has been, not in the spiritual vision of the Pre-Raphaelites, for all their marvel of Greek legend and their mystery of Italian song, but in the work of such men as Whistler and Albert Moore, who have raised design and colour to the ideal level of poetry and music. For the quality of their exquisite painting comes from the mere inventive and creative handling of line and colour, from a certain form and choice of beautiful workmanship, which, rejecting all literary reminiscence and all metaphysical idea, is in itself entirely satisfying to the aesthetic sense—is, as the Greeks would say, an end in itself; the effect of their work being like the effect given to us by music; for music is the art in which form and matter are always one—the art whose subject cannot be separated from the method of its expression; the art which most completely realizes for us the artistic ideal, and is the condition to which all the other arts are constantly aspiring.

Now, this increased sense of the absolutely satisfying value of beautiful workmanship, this recognition of the primary importance of the sensuous element in art, this love of art for art's sake, is the point in which we of the younger school have made a departure from the teaching of Mr. Ruskin,—a departure definite and different and decisive.

Master indeed of the knowledge of all noble living and of the wisdom of all spiritual things will he be to us ever, seeing that it was he who by the magic of his presence and the music of his lips taught us at Oxford that enthusiasm for beauty which is the secret of Hellenism, and that desire for creation which is the secret of life, and filled some of us, at least, with the lofty and passionate ambition to go forth into far and fair lands with some message for the nations and some mission for the world, and yet in his art criticism, his estimate of the joyous element of art, his whole method of approaching art, we are no longer with him; for the keystone to his aesthetic system is ethical always. He would judge of a picture by the amount of noble moral ideas it expresses; but to us the channels by which all noble work in painting can touch, and does touch, the soul are not those of truths of life or metaphysical truths. To him perfection of workmanship seems but the symbol of pride, and incompleteness of technical resource the image of an imagination too limitless to find within the limits of form its complete expression, or of love too simple not to stammer in its tale. But to us the rule of art is not the rule of morals. In an ethical system, indeed, of any gentle mercy good intentions will, one is fain to fancy, have their recognition; but of those that would enter the serene House of Beauty the question that we ask is not what they had ever meant to do, but what they have done. Their pathetic intentions are of no value to us, but their realized creations only. Pour moi je prefere les poetes qui font des vers, les medecins qui sachent guerir, les peintres qui sanchent peindre.

Nor, in looking at a work of art, should we be dreaming of what it symbolises, but rather loving it for what it is. Indeed, the transcendental spirit is alien to the spirit of art. The metaphysical mind of Asia may create for itself the monstrous and many-breasted idol, but to the Greek, pure artist, that work is most instinct with spiritual life which conforms most closely to the perfect facts of physical life also. Nor, in its primary aspect, has a painting, for

230

istance, any more spiritual message or meaning for us than a blue tile from
ie wall of Damascus, or a Hitzen vase. It is a beautifully coloured surface,
othing more, and affects us by no suggestion stolen from philosophy, no
athos pilfered from literature, no feeling filched from a poet, but by its own
ncommunicable artistic essence—by that selection of truth which we call
tyle, and that relation of values which is the draughtsmanship of painting,
y the whole quality of the workmanship, the arabesque of the design, the
plendour of the colour, for these things are enough to stir the most divine
nd remote of the chords which make music in our soul, and colour, indeed,
of itself a mystical presence on things, and tone a kind of sentiment . . . all
iese poems aim, as I said, at producing a purely artistic effect, and have the
are and exquisite quality that belongs to work of that kind; and I feel that
ie entire subordination in our aesthetic movement of all merely emotional
nd intellectual motives to the vital informing poetic principle is the surest
ign of our strength.

But it is not enough that a work of art should conform to the aesthetic
emands of the age: there should be also about it, if it is to give us any
ermanent delight, the impress of a distinct individuality. Whatever work
ve have in the nineteenth century must rest on the two poles of personality
nd perfection. And so in this little volume, by separating the earlier and
nore simple work from the work that is later and stronger and possesses
ncreased technical power and more artistic vision, one might weave these
isconnected poems, these stray and scattered threads, into one fiery-
oloured strand of life, noting first a boy's mere gladness of being young,
vith all its simple joy in field and flower, in sunlight and in song, and then
he bitterness of sudden sorrow at the ending by Death of one of the brief
nd beautiful friendships of one's youth, with all those unanswered lodgings
nd questionings unsatisfied by which we vex, so uselessly, the marble face of
eath; the artistic contrast between the discontented incompleteness of the
pirit and the complete perfection of the style that expresses it forming the
hief element of the aesthetic charm of these particular poems;—and then the
irth of Love, and all the wonder and the fear and the perilous delight of one
n whose boyish brows the little wings of love have beaten for the first time;
nd the love-songs, so dainty and delicate, little swallow-flights of music, and

full of such fragrance and freedom that they might all be sung in the open ai and across moving water; and then autumn, coming with its choirless wood and odorous decay and ruined loveliness, Love lying dead; and the sense c the mere pity of it.

One might stop there, for from a young poet one should ask for n deeper chords of life than those that love and friendship make eternal fo us; and the best poems in the volume belong clearly to a later time, a tim when these real experiences become absorbed and gathered up into a forr which seems from such real experiences to be the most alien and the mos remote; when the simple expression of joy or sorrow suffices no longer, an lives rather in the stateliness of the cadenced metre, in the music and colou of the linked words, than in any direct utterance; lives, one might say, i the perfection of the form more than in the pathos of the feeling. And ye after the broken music of love and the burial of love in the autumn wood: we can trace that wandering among strange people, and in lands unknow: to us, by which we try so pathetically to heal the hurts of the life we knov and that pure and passionate devotion to Art which one gets when the hars! reality of life has too suddenly wounded one, and is with discontent or sorrov marring one's youth, just as often, I think, as one gets it from any natura joy of living; and that curious intensity of vision by which, in moments c overmastering sadness and despair ungovernable, artistic things will live i: one's memory with a vivid realism caught from the life which they help on to forget— an old grey tomb in Flanders with a strange legend on it, makin one think how, perhaps, passion does live on after death; a necklace of blu and amber beads and a broken mirror found in a girl's grave at Rome, marble image of a boy habited like Eros, and with the pathetic tradition of great king's sorrow lingering about it like a purple shadow,—over all these th tired spirit broods with that calm and certain joy that one gets when one ha found something that the ages never dull and the world cannot harm; an‹ with it comes that desire of Greek things which is often an artistic method o expressing one's desire for perfection; and that longing for the old dead day which is so modern, so incomplete, so touching, being, in a way, the inverte‹ torch of Hope, which burns the hand it should guide; and for many things little sadness, and for all things a great love; and lastly, in the pinewood by th sea, once more the quick and vital pulse of joyous youth leaping and laughing in every line, the frank and fearless freedom of wave and wind waking into fire life's burnt-out ashes and into song the silent lips of pain,—how clearly one seems to see it all, the long colonnade of pines with sea and sky peeping in here and there like a flitting of silver; the open place in the green, deep heart of the wood with the little moss-grown altar to the old Italian god in it; and the flowers all about, cyclamen in the shadowy places, and the stars of the white narcissus lying like snow-flakes over the grass, where the quick, bright-eyed lizard starts by the stone, and the snake lies coiled lazily in the sun on the hot sand, and overhead the gossamer floats from the branches like thin, tremulous threads of gold,—the scene is so perfect for its motive, for surely here, if anywhere, the real gladness of life might be revealed to one's youth— the gladness that comes, not from the rejection, but from the absorption, of all passion, and is like that serene calm that dwells in the faces of the Greek statues, and which despair and sorrow cannot touch, but intensify only.

In some such way as this we could gather up these strewn and scattered petals of song into one perfect rose of life, and yet, perhaps, in so doing, we might be missing the true quality of the poems; one's real life is so often the life that one does not lead; and beautiful poems, like threads of beautiful silks, may be woven into many patterns and to suit many designs, all wonderful and all different: and romantic poetry, too, is essentially the poetry of impressions, being like that latest school of painting, the school of Whistler and Albert Moore, in its choice of situation as opposed to subject; in its dealing with the exceptions rather than with the types of life; in its brief intensity; in what one might call its fiery-coloured momentariness, it being indeed the momentary situations of life, the momentary aspects of nature, which poetry and painting new seek to render for us. Sincerity and constancy will the artist, indeed, have always; but sincerity in art is merely that plastic perfection of execution without which a poem or a painting, however noble its sentiment or human its origin, is but wasted and unreal work, and the constancy of the artist cannot be to any definite rule or system of living, but to that principle of beauty only through which the inconstant shadows of his life are in their most fleeting moment arrested and made permanent. He will not, for instance, in intellectual matters acquiesce in that facile orthodoxy of our day which is so reasonable and so artistically uninteresting, nor yet will he desire that fiery faith of the antique time which, while it intensified, yet limited the vision; still less will he allow the calm of his culture to be marred by the discordant despair of doubt or the sadness of a sterile scepticism; for the Valley Perilous, where ignorant armies clash by night, is no resting-place meet for her to whom the gods have assigned the clear upland, the serene height, and the sunlit air,— rather will he be always curiously testing new forms of belief, tinging his nature with the sentiment that still lingers about some beautiful creeds, and searching for experience itself, and not for the fruits of experience; when he has got its secret, he will leave without regret much that was once very precious to him. "I am always insincere," says Emerson somewhere, "as knowing that there are other moods": "Les emotions," wrote Theophile Gautier once in a review of Arsene Houssaye, "Les emotions, ne se ressemblent pas, mais etre emu—voila l'important."

Now, this is the secret of the art of the modern romantic school, and gives one the right keynote for its apprehension; but the real quality of all work which, like Mr. Rodd's, aims, as I said, at a purely artistic effect, cannot be described in terms of intellectual criticism; it is too intangible for that. One can perhaps convey it best in terms of the other arts, and by reference to them; and, indeed, some of these poems are as iridescent and as exquisite as a lovely fragment of Venetian glass; others as delicate in perfect workmanship and as single in natural motive as an etching by Whistler is, or one of those beautiful little Greek figures which in the olive woods round Tanagra men can still find, with the faint gilding and the fading crimson not yet fled from hair and lips and raiment; and many of them seem like one of Corot's twilights just passing into music; for not merely in visible colour, but in sentiment also—which is the colour of poetry—may there be a kind of tone.

But I think that the best likeness to the quality of this young poet's work I ever saw was in the landscape by the Loire. We were staying once, he and I, at Amboise, that little village with its grey slate roofs and steep streets and gaunt, grim gateway, where the quiet cottages nestle like white pigeons into the sombre clefts of the great bastioned rock, and the stately Renaissance houses stand silent and apart—very desolate now, but with some memory of the old days still lingering about the delicately-twisted pillars, and the carved doorways, with their grotesque animals, and laughing masks, and quaint heraldic devices, all reminding one of a people who could not think life real till they had made it fantastic. And above the village, and beyond the bend of the river, we used to go in the afternoon, and sketch from one of the big barges that bring the wine in autumn and the wood in winter down to the sea, or lie in the long grass and make plans pour la gloire, et pour ennuyer les Philistins, or wander along the low, sedgy banks, "matching our reeds in sportive rivalry," as comrades used in the old Sicilian days; and the land was an ordinary land enough, and bare, too, when one thought of Italy, and how the oleanders were robing the hillsides by Genoa in scarlet, and the cyclamen filling with its purple every valley from Florence to Rome; for there was not much real beauty, perhaps, in it, only long, white dusty roads and straight rows of formal poplars; but, now and then, some little breaking gleam of broken light would lend to the grey field and the silent barn a secret and a mystery that were hardly their own, would transfigure for one exquisite moment the peasants passing down through the vineyard, or the shepherd watching on the hill, would tip the willows with silver and touch the river into gold; and the wonder of the effect, with the strange simplicity of the material, always seemed to me to be a little like the quality of these the verses of my friend.

About Author

Oscar Fingal O'Flahertie Wills Wilde (16 October 1854 – 30 November 1900) was an Irish poet and playwright. After writing in different forms throughout the 1880s, the early 1890s saw him become one of the most popular playwrights in London. He is best remembered for his epigrams and plays, his novel The Picture of Dorian Gray, and the circumstances of his criminal conviction for "gross indecency", imprisonment, and early death at age 46.

Wilde's parents were successful Anglo-Irish intellectuals in Dublin. A young Wilde learned to speak fluent French and German. At university, Wilde read Greats; he demonstrated himself to be an exceptional classicist, first at Trinity College Dublin, then at Oxford. He became associated with the emerging philosophy of aestheticism, led by two of his tutors, Walter Pater and John Ruskin. After university, Wilde moved to London into fashionable cultural and social circles.

As a spokesman for aestheticism, he tried his hand at various literary activities: he published a book of poems, lectured in the United States and Canada on the new "English Renaissance in Art" and interior decoration, and then returned to London where he worked prolifically as a journalist. Known for his biting wit, flamboyant dress and glittering conversational skill, Wilde became one of the best-known personalities of his day. At the turn of the 1890s, he refined his ideas about the supremacy of art in a series of dialogues and essays, and incorporated themes of decadence, duplicity, and beauty into what would be his only novel, The Picture of Dorian Gray (1890). The opportunity to construct aesthetic details precisely, and combine them with larger social themes, drew Wilde to write drama. He wrote Salome (1891) in French while in Paris but it was refused a licence for England due to an absolute prohibition on the portrayal of Biblical subjects on the English stage. Unperturbed, Wilde produced four society comedies in the early 1890s, which made him one of the most successful playwrights of late-Victorian London.

At the height of his fame and success, while The Importance of Being Earnest (1895) was still being performed in London, Wilde had the Marques of Queensberry prosecuted for criminal libel. The Marquess was the father of Wilde's lover, Lord Alfred Douglas. The libel trial unearthed evidence that caused Wilde to drop his charges and led to his own arrest and trial for gross indecency with men. After two more trials he was convicted and sentenced to two years' hard labour, the maximum penalty, and was jailed from 189 to 1897. During his last year in prison, he wrote De Profundis (published posthumously in 1905), a long letter which discusses his spiritual journe through his trials, forming a dark counterpoint to his earlier philosophy of pleasure. On his release, he left immediately for France, never to return t Ireland or Britain. There he wrote his last work, The Ballad of Reading Gao (1898), a long poem commemorating the harsh rhythms of prison life.

Early life

Oscar Wilde was born at 21 Westland Row, Dublin (now home of th Oscar Wilde Centre, Trinity College), the second of three children born t Anglo-Irish Sir William Wilde and Jane Wilde, two years behind his brother William ("Willie"). Wilde's mother had distant Italian ancestry,and unde the pseudonym "Speranza" (the Italian word for 'hope'), wrote poetry for th revolutionary Young Irelanders in 1848; she was a lifelong Irish nationalis She read the Young Irelanders' poetry to Oscar and Willie, inculcating a lov of these poets in her sons. Lady Wilde's interest in the neo-classical reviva showed in the paintings and busts of ancient Greece and Rome in her home

William Wilde was Ireland's leading oto-ophthalmologic (ear an eye) surgeon and was knighted in 1864 for his services as medical advise and assistant commissioner to the censuses of Ireland. He also wrote book about Irish archaeology and peasant folklore. A renowned philanthropis his dispensary for the care of the city's poor at the rear of Trinity College Dublin, was the forerunner of the Dublin Eye and Ear Hospital, nov located at Adelaide Road. On his father's side Wilde was descended fror a Dutchman, Colonel de Wilde, who went to Ireland with King Williar of Orange's invading army in 1690, and numerous Anglo-Irish ancestors On his mother's side, Wilde's ancestors included a bricklayer from Count Durham, who emigrated to Ireland sometime in the 1770s.

Wilde was baptised as an infant in St. Mark's Church, Dublin, the local Church of Ireland (Anglican) church. When the church was closed, the records were moved to the nearby St. Ann's Church, Dawson Street. Davis Coakley mentions a second baptism by a Catholic priest, Father Prideaux Fox, who befriended Oscar's mother circa 1859. According to Fox's testimony in Donahoe's Magazine in 1905, Jane Wilde would visit his chapel in Glencree, County Wicklow, for Mass and would take her sons with her. She asked Father Fox in this period to baptise her sons.

Fox described it in this way:

> "I am not sure if she ever became a Catholic herself but it was not long before she asked me to instruct two of her children, one of them being the future erratic genius, Oscar Wilde. After a few weeks I baptized these two children, Lady Wilde herself being present on the occasion.

In addition to his children with his wife, Sir William Wilde was the father of three children born out of wedlock before his marriage: Henry Wilson, born in 1838 to one woman, and Emily and Mary Wilde, born in 1847 and 1849, respectively, to a second woman. Sir William acknowledged paternity of his illegitimate or "natural" children and provided for their education, arranging for them to be reared by his relatives rather than with his legitimate children in his family household with his wife.

In 1855, the family moved to No. 1 Merrion Square, where Wilde's sister, Isola, was born in 1857. The Wildes' new home was larger. With both his parents' success and delight in social life, the house soon became the site of a "unique medical and cultural milieu". Guests at their salon included Sheridan Le Fanu, Charles Lever, George Petrie, Isaac Butt, William Rowan Hamilton and Samuel Ferguson.

Until he was nine, Oscar Wilde was educated at home, where a French nursemaid and a German governess taught him their languages. He attended Portora Royal School in Enniskillen, County Fermanagh, from 1864 to 1871. Until his early twenties, Wilde summered at the villa, Moytura House, which his father had built in Cong, County Mayo. There the young Wilde and his brother Willie played with George Moore.

Isola died at age nine of meningitis. Wilde's poem "Requiescat" i written to her memory.

"Tread lightly, she is near

Under the snow

Speak gently, she can hear

the daisies grow"

University education: 1870s

Trinity College, Dublin

Wilde left Portora with a royal scholarship to read classics at Trinity College, Dublin, from 1871 to 1874, sharing rooms with his older brother Willie Wilde. Trinity, one of the leading classical schools, placed him with scholars such as R. Y. Tyrell, Arthur Palmer, Edward Dowden and his tutor Professor J. P. Mahaffy, who inspired his interest in Greek literature. As a student Wilde worked with Mahaffy on the latter's book Social Life in Greece. Wilde, despite later reservations, called Mahaffy "my first and best teacher" and "the scholar who showed me how to love Greek things".For his part Mahaffy boasted of having created Wilde; later, he said Wilde was "the only blot on my tutorship".

The University Philosophical Society also provided an education, a members discussed intellectual and artistic subjects such as Dante Gabrie Rossetti and Algernon Charles Swinburne weekly. Wilde quickly became an established member – the members' suggestion book for 1874 contains two pages of banter (sportingly) mocking Wilde's emergent aestheticism. He presented a paper titled "Aesthetic Morality". At Trinity, Wilde established himself as an outstanding student: he came first in his class in his first year won a scholarship by competitive examination in his second and, in his finals won the Berkeley Gold Medal in Greek, the University's highest academic award. He was encouraged to compete for a demyship to Magdalen College Oxford – which he won easily, having already studied Greek for over nine years.

Magdalen College, Oxford

At Magdalen, he read Greats from 1874 to 1878, and from there he applied to join the Oxford Union, but failed to be elected.

Attracted by its dress, secrecy, and ritual, Wilde petitioned the Apollo Masonic Lodge at Oxford, and was soon raised to the "Sublime Degree of Master Mason".During a resurgent interest in Freemasonry in his third year, he commented he "would be awfully sorry to give it up if I secede from the Protestant Heresy". Wilde's active involvement in Freemasonry lasted only for the time he spent at Oxford; he allowed his membership of the Apollo University Lodge to lapse after failing to pay subscriptions.

Catholicism deeply appealed to him, especially its rich liturgy, and he discussed converting to it with clergy several times. In 1877, Wilde was left speechless after an audience with Pope Pius IX in Rome.He eagerly read the books of Cardinal Newman, a noted Anglican priest who had converted to Catholicism and risen in the church hierarchy. He became more serious in 1878, when he met the Reverend Sebastian Bowden, a priest in the Brompton Oratory who had received some high-profile converts. Neither his father, who threatened to cut off his funds, nor Mahaffy thought much of the plan; but mostly Wilde, the supreme individualist, balked at the last minute from pledging himself to any formal creed. On the appointed day of his baptism, Wilde sent Father Bowden a bunch of altar lilies instead. Wilde did retain a lifelong interest in Catholic theology and liturgy.

While at Magdalen College, Wilde became particularly well known for his role in the aesthetic and decadent movements. He wore his hair long, openly scorned "manly" sports though he occasionally boxed, and he decorated his rooms with peacock feathers, lilies, sunflowers, blue china and other objets d'art. He once remarked to friends, whom he entertained lavishly, "I find it harder and harder every day to live up to my blue china." The line quickly became famous, accepted as a slogan by aesthetes but used against them by critics who sensed in it a terrible vacuousness. Some elements disdained the aesthetes, but their languishing attitudes and showy costumes became a recognised pose. Wilde was once physically attacked by a group of four fellow students, and dealt with them single-handedly, surprising critics. By his third year Wilde had truly begun to develop himself and his myth, and considered his learning to be more expansive than what was within the prescribed texts. This attitude resulted in his being rusticated for one term, after he had returned late to a college term from a trip to Greece with Mahaffy.

Wilde did not meet Walter Pater until his third year, but had been enthralled by his Studies in the History of the Renaissance, published during Wilde's final year in Trinity. Pater argued that man's sensibility to beauty should be refined above all else, and that each moment should be felt to its fullest extent. Years later, in De Profundis, Wilde described Pater's Studies... as "that book that has had such a strange influence over my life".He learned tracts of the book by heart, and carried it with him on travels in later years. Pater gave Wilde his sense of almost flippant devotion to art, though he gained a purpose for it through the lectures and writings of critic John Ruskin. Ruskin despaired at the self-validating aestheticism of Pater, arguing that the importance of art lies in its potential for the betterment of society. Ruskin admired beauty, but believed it must be allied with, and applied to, moral good. When Wilde eagerly attended Ruskin's lecture series The Aesthetic and Mathematic Schools of Art in Florence, he learned about aesthetics as the non-mathematical elements of painting. Despite being given to neither early rising nor manual labour, Wilde volunteered for Ruskin's project to convert a swampy country lane into a smart road neatly edged with flowers.

Wilde won the 1878 Newdigate Prize for his poem "Ravenna", which reflected on his visit there the year before, and he duly read it at Encaenia. In November 1878, he graduated with a double first in his B.A. of Classical Moderations and Literae Humaniores (Greats). Wilde wrote to a friend, "The dons are 'astonied' beyond words – the Bad Boy doing so well in the end!"

Apprenticeship of an aesthete: 1880s

Debut in society

After graduation from Oxford, Wilde returned to Dublin, where he met again Florence Balcombe, a childhood sweetheart. She became engaged to Bram Stoker and they married in 1878. Wilde was disappointed but stoic:

he wrote to her, remembering "the two sweet years – the sweetest years of all my youth" during which they had been close. He also stated his intention to "return to England, probably for good." This he did in 1878, only briefly visiting Ireland twice after that.

Unsure of his next step, Wilde wrote to various acquaintances enquiring about Classics positions at Oxford or Cambridge. The Rise of Historical Criticism was his submission for the Chancellor's Essay prize of 1879, which, though no longer a student, he was still eligible to enter. Its subject, "Historical Criticism among the Ancients" seemed ready-made for Wilde – with both his skill in composition and ancient learning – but he struggled to find his voice with the long, flat, scholarly style. Unusually, no prize was awarded that year.

With the last of his inheritance from the sale of his father's houses, he set himself up as a bachelor in London. The 1881 British Census listed Wilde as a boarder at 1 (now 44) Tite Street, Chelsea, where Frank Miles, a society painter, was the head of the household. Wilde spent the next six years in London and Paris, and in the United States, where he travelled to deliver lectures.

He had been publishing lyrics and poems in magazines since entering Trinity College, especially in Kottabos and the Dublin University Magazine. In mid-1881, at 27 years old, he published Poems, which collected, revised and expanded his poems.

The book was generally well received, and sold out its first print run of 750 copies. Punch was less enthusiastic, saying "The poet is Wilde, but his poetry's tame". By a tight vote, the Oxford Union condemned the book for alleged plagiarism. The librarian, who had requested the book for the library, returned the presentation copy to Wilde with a note of apology.Biographer Richard Ellmann argues that Wilde's poem "Hélas!" was a sincere, though flamboyant, attempt to explain the dichotomies the poet saw in himself; one line reads: "To drift with every passion till my soul

Is a stringed lute on which all winds can play".

The book had further printings in 1882. It was bound in a rich, enamel parchment cover (embossed with gilt blossom) and printed on hand-made Dutch paper; over the next few years, Wilde presented many copies to the dignitaries and writers who received him during his lecture tours.

America: 1882

Aestheticism was sufficiently in vogue to be caricatured by Gilbert and Sullivan in Patience (1881). Richard D'Oyly Carte, an English impresario, invited Wilde to make a lecture tour of North America, simultaneously priming the pump for the US tour of Patience and selling this most charming aesthete to the American public. Wilde journeyed on the SS Arizona, arriving 2 January 1882, and disembarking the following day. Originally planned to last four months, it continued for almost a year due to the commercial success. Wilde sought to transpose the beauty he saw in art into daily life. This was a practical as well as philosophical project: in Oxford he had surrounded himself with blue china and lilies, and now one of his lectures was on interior design.

When asked to explain reports that he had paraded down Piccadilly in London carrying a lily, long hair flowing, Wilde replied, "It's not whether I did it or not that's important, but whether people believed I did it". Wilde believed that the artist should hold forth higher ideals, and that pleasure and beauty would replace utilitarian ethics.

Wilde and aestheticism were both mercilessly caricatured and criticised in the press; the Springfield Republican, for instance, commented on Wilde's behaviour during his visit to Boston to lecture on aestheticism, suggesting that Wilde's conduct was more a bid for notoriety rather than devotion to beauty and the aesthetic. T. W. Higginson, a cleric and abolitionist, wrote in "Unmanly Manhood" of his general concern that Wilde, "whose only distinction is that he has written a thin volume of very mediocre verse" would improperly influence the behaviour of men and women.

According to biographer Michèle Mendelssohn, Wilde was the subject of anti-Irish caricature and was portrayed as a monkey, a blackface performer and a Christy's Minstrel throughout his career. "Harper's Weekly put a sunflower worshipping monkey dressed as Wilde on the front of the January 1882 issue. The magazine didn't let its reputation for quality impede its expression of what are now considered odious ethnic and racial ideologies. The drawing stimulated other American maligners and, in England, had a full-page reprint in the Lady's Pictorial. ... When the National Republican discussed Wilde, it was to explain 'a few items as to the animal's pedigree.' And on 22 January 1882 the Washington Post illustrated the Wild Man of Borneo alongside Oscar Wilde of England and asked 'How far is it from this to this?' "Though his press reception was hostile, Wilde was well received in diverse settings across America; he drank whiskey with miners in Leadville, Colorado, and was fêted at the most fashionable salons in many cities he visited.

London life and marriage

His earnings, plus expected income from The Duchess of Padua, allowed him to move to Paris between February and mid-May 1883. While there he met Robert Sherard, whom he entertained constantly. "We are dining on the Duchess tonight", Wilde would declare before taking him to an expensive restaurant. In August he briefly returned to New York for the production of Vera, his first play, after it was turned down in London. He reportedly entertained the other passengers with "Ave Imperatrix!, A Poem on England", about the rise and fall of empires. E. C. Stedman, in Victorian Poets, describes this "lyric to England" as "manly verse – a poetic and eloquent invocation". The play was initially well received by the audience, but when the critics wrote lukewarm reviews, attendance fell sharply and the play closed a week after it had opened.

Wilde had to return to England, where he continued to lecture on topics including Personal Impressions of America, The Value of Art in Modern Life, and Dress.

In London, he had been introduced in 1881 to Constance Lloyd, daughter of Horace Lloyd, a wealthy Queen's Counsel, and his wife. She happened to be visiting Dublin in 1884, when Wilde was lecturing at the Gaiety Theatre. He proposed to her, and they married on 29 May 1884 at the Anglican St James's Church, Paddington, in London. Although Constance had an annual allowance of £250, which was generous for a young woman (equivalent to about £25,600 in current value), the Wildes had relatively luxurious tastes. They had preached to others for so long on the subject of design that people expected their home to set new standards. No. 16, Tite Street was duly renovated in seven months at considerable expense. The couple had two sons together, Cyril (1885) and Vyvyan (1886). Wilde became the sole literary signatory of George Bernard Shaw's petition for a pardon of the anarchists arrested (and later executed) after the Haymarket massacre in Chicago in 1886.

Robert Ross had read Wilde's poems before they met at Oxford in 1886. He seemed unrestrained by the Victorian prohibition against homosexuality and became estranged from his family. By Richard Ellmann's account, he was a precocious seventeen-year-old who "so young and yet so knowing, was determined to seduce Wilde". According to Daniel Mendelsohn, Wilde, who had long alluded to Greek love, was "initiated into homosexual sex" by Ross while his "marriage had begun to unravel after his wife's second pregnancy, which left him physically repelled".

Prose writing: 1886–91

Journalism and editorship: 1886–89

Criticism over artistic matters in The Pall Mall Gazette provoked a letter in self-defence, and soon Wilde was a contributor to that and other journals during 1885–87. He enjoyed reviewing and journalism; the form suited his style. He could organise and share his views on art, literature and life, yet in a format less tedious than lecturing. Buoyed up, his reviews were largely chatty and positive.Wilde, like his parents before him, also supported the cause of Irish nationalism. When Charles Stewart Parnell was falsely accused of inciting murder, Wilde wrote a series of astute columns defending him in the Daily Chronicle.

His flair, having previously been put mainly into socialising, suited journalism and rapidly attracted notice. With his youth nearly over, and a family to support, in mid-1887 Wilde became the editor of The Lady's World magazine, his name prominently appearing on the cover.He promptly enamed it as The Woman's World and raised its tone, adding serious articles on parenting, culture, and politics, while keeping discussions of fashion and arts. Two pieces of fiction were usually included, one to be read to children, the other for the ladies themselves. Wilde worked hard to solicit good contributions from his wide artistic acquaintance, including those of Lady Wilde and his wife Constance, while his own "Literary and Other Notes" were themselves popular and amusing.

The initial vigour and excitement which he brought to the job began to fade as administration, commuting and office life became tedious. At the same time as Wilde's interest flagged, the publishers became concerned anew about circulation: sales, at the relatively high price of one shilling, remained low. Increasingly sending instructions to the magazine by letter, Wilde began a new period of creative work and his own column appeared less regularly.In October 1889, Wilde had finally found his voice in prose and, at the end of the second volume, Wilde left The Woman's World. The magazine outlasted him by one issue.

If Wilde's period at the helm of the magazine was a mixed success from an organizational point of view, it played a pivotal role in his development as a writer and facilitated his ascent to fame. Whilst Wilde the journalist supplied articles under the guidance of his editors, Wilde the editor was forced to learn to manipulate the literary marketplace on his own terms.

During the late 1880s, Wilde was a close friend of the artist James McNeill Whistler and they dined together on many occasions. At one of these dinners, Whistler said a bon mot that Wilde found particularly witty, Wilde exclaimed that he wished that he had said it, and Whistler retorted "You will, Oscar, you will".Herbert Vivian—a mutual friend of Wilde and Whistler— attended the dinner and recorded it in his article The Reminiscences of a Short Life which appeared in The Sun in 1889. The article alleged that Wilde had a habit of passing off other people's witticisms as his own—especially Whistler's. Wilde considered Vivian's article to be a scurrilous betrayal, and it directly caused the broken friendship between Wilde and Whistler. The Reminiscences also caused great acrimony between Wilde and Vivian, Wilde accusing Vivian of "the inaccuracy of an eavesdropper with the method of a blackmailer" and banishing Vivian from his circle.

Shorter fiction

Wilde published The Happy Prince and Other Tales in 1888, and had been regularly writing fairy stories for magazines. In 1891 he published two more collections, Lord Arthur Savile's Crime and Other Stories, and in September A House of Pomegranates was dedicated "To Constance Mary Wilde". "The Portrait of Mr. W. H.", which Wilde had begun in 1887, was first published in Blackwood's Edinburgh Magazine in July 1889. It is a short story, which reports a conversation, in which the theory that Shakespeare's sonnets were written out of the poet's love of the boy actor "Willie Hughes", is advanced, retracted, and then propounded again. The only evidence for this is two supposed puns within the sonnets themselves.

The anonymous narrator is at first sceptical, then believing, finally flirtatious with the reader: he concludes that "there is really a great deal to be said of the Willie Hughes theory of Shakespeare's sonnets." By the end fact and fiction have melded together. Arthur Ransome wrote that Wilde "read something of himself into Shakespeare's sonnets" and became fascinated with the "Willie Hughes theory" despite the lack of biographical evidence for the historical William Hughes' existence. Instead of writing a short but serious essay on the question, Wilde tossed the theory amongst the three characters of the story, allowing it to unfold as background to the plot. The story thus is an early masterpiece of Wilde's combining many elements that interested him: conversation, literature and the idea that to shed oneself of an idea one must first convince another of its truth. Ransome concludes that Wilde succeeds precisely because the literary criticism is unveiled with such a deft touch.

Though containing nothing but "special pleading", it would not, he says "be possible to build an airier castle in Spain than this of the imaginary William Hughes" we continue listening nonetheless to be charmed by the telling. "You must believe in Willie Hughes," Wilde told an acquaintance, "I almost do, myself."

Essays and dialogues

Wilde, having tired of journalism, had been busy setting out his aesthetic ideas more fully in a series of longer prose pieces which were published in the major literary-intellectual journals of the day. In January 1889, The Decay of Lying: A Dialogue appeared in The Nineteenth Century, and Pen, Pencil and Poison, a satirical biography of Thomas Griffiths Wainewright, in The Fortnightly Review, edited by Wilde's friend Frank Harris. Two of Wilde's four writings on aesthetics are dialogues: though Wilde had evolved professionally from lecturer to writer, he retained an oral tradition of sorts. Having always excelled as a wit and raconteur, he often composed by assembling phrases, bons mots and witticisms into a longer, cohesive work.

Wilde was concerned about the effect of moralising on art; he believed in art's redemptive, developmental powers: "Art is individualism, and individualism is a disturbing and disintegrating force. There lies its immense value. For what it seeks is to disturb monotony of type, slavery of custom, tyranny of habit, and the reduction of man to the level of a machine." In his only political text, The Soul of Man Under Socialism, he argued political conditions should establish this primacy – private property should be abolished, and cooperation should be substituted for competition. At the same time, he stressed that the government most amenable to artists was no government at all. Wilde envisioned a society where mechanisation has freed human effort from the burden of necessity, effort which can instead be expended on artistic creation. George Orwell summarised, "In effect, the world will be populated by artists, each striving after perfection in the way that seems best to him."

This point of view did not align him with the Fabians, intellectual socialists who advocated using state apparatus to change social conditions, nor did it endear him to the monied classes whom he had previously entertained. Hesketh Pearson, introducing a collection of Wilde's essays in 1950, remarked how The Soul of Man Under Socialism had been an inspirational text for revolutionaries in Tsarist Russia but laments that in the Stalinist era "it is doubtful whether there are any uninspected places in which it could now be hidden".

Wilde considered including this pamphlet and The Portrait of Mr. W.H., his essay-story on Shakespeare's sonnets, in a new anthology in 1891, but eventually decided to limit it to purely aesthetic subjects. Intentions packaged

revisions of four essays: The Decay of Lying, Pen, Pencil and Poison, Th
Truth of Masks (first published 1885), and The Critic as Artist in two part
For Pearson the biographer, the essays and dialogues exhibit every aspect (
Wilde's genius and character: wit, romancer, talker, lecturer, humanist an
scholar and concludes that "no other productions of his have as varied a
appeal". 1891 turned out to be Wilde's annus mirabilis; apart from his thre
collections he also produced his only novel.

The Picture of Dorian Gray

The first version of The Picture of Dorian Gray was published as the lea
story in the July 1890 edition of Lippincott's Monthly Magazine, along wit
five others. The story begins with a man painting a picture of Gray. Whe
Gray, who has a "face like ivory and rose leaves", sees his finished portrai
he breaks down. Distraught that his beauty will fade while the portra
stays beautiful, he inadvertently makes a Faustian bargain in which only th
painted image grows old while he stays beautiful and young. For Wilde, th
purpose of art would be to guide life as if beauty alone were its object. A
Gray's portrait allows him to escape the corporeal ravages of his hedonism
Wilde sought to juxtapose the beauty he saw in art with daily life.

Reviewers immediately criticised the novel's decadence and homosexu;
allusions; The Daily Chronicle for example, called it "unclean", "poisonous"
and "heavy with the mephitic odours of moral and spiritual putrefaction"
Which he clarified his stance on ethics and aesthetics in art – "If a wor
of art is rich and vital and complete, those who have artistic instincts wi
see its beauty and those to whom ethics appeal more strongly will see i
moral lesson." He nevertheless revised it extensively for book publicatio
in 1891: six new chapters were added, some overtly decadent passages an
homo-eroticism excised, and a preface was included consisting of twenty tw
epigrams, such as "Books are well written, or badly written. That is all."

Contemporary reviewers and modern critics have postulated numerou
possible sources of the story, a search Jershua McCormack argues is futil
because Wilde "has tapped a root of Western folklore so deep and ubiquitou
that the story has escaped its origins and returned to the oral tradition." Wild

claimed the plot was "an idea that is as old as the history of literature but to which I have given a new form".Modern critic Robin McKie considered the novel to be technically mediocre, saying that the conceit of the plot had guaranteed its fame, but the device is never pushed to its full.On the other hand, Robert McCrum of The Guardian deemed it the 27th best novel ever written in English, calling it "an arresting, and slightly camp, exercise in late-Victorian gothic."

Theatrical career: 1892–95

Salomé

The 1891 census records the Wildes' residence at 16 Tite Street, where he lived with his wife Constance and two sons. Wilde though, not content with being better known than ever in London, returned to Paris in October 1891, this time as a respected writer. He was received at the salons littéraires, including the famous mardis of Stéphane Mallarmé, a renowned symbolist poet of the time. Wilde's two plays during the 1880s, Vera; or, The Nihilists and The Duchess of Padua, had not met with much success. He had continued his interest in the theatre and now, after finding his voice in prose, his thoughts turned again to the dramatic form as the biblical iconography of Salome filled his mind. One evening, after discussing depictions of Salome throughout history, he returned to his hotel and noticed a blank copybook lying on the desk, and it occurred to him to write in it what he had been saying. The result was a new play, Salomé, written rapidly and in French.

A tragedy, it tells the story of Salome, the stepdaughter of the tetrarch Herod Antipas, who, to her stepfather's dismay but mother's delight, requests the head of Jokanaan (John the Baptist) on a silver platter as a reward for dancing the Dance of the Seven Veils. When Wilde returned to London just before Christmas the Paris Echo referred to him as "le great event" of the season. Rehearsals of the play, starring Sarah Bernhardt, began but the play was refused a licence by the Lord Chamberlain, since it depicted biblical characters. Salome was published jointly in Paris and London in 1893, but was not performed until 1896 in Paris, during Wilde's later incarceration.

Comedies of society

Wilde, who had first set out to irritate Victorian society with his dress and talking points, then outrage it with Dorian Gray, his novel of vice hidden beneath art, finally found a way to critique society on its own terms. Lady Windermere's Fan was first performed on 20 February 1892 at St James' Theatre, packed with the cream of society. On the surface a witty comedy, there is subtle subversion underneath: "it concludes with collusive concealment rather than collective disclosure". The audience, like Lady Windermere, are forced to soften harsh social codes in favour of a more nuanced view. The play was enormously popular, touring the country for months, but largely trashed by conservative critics. It was followed by A Woman of No Importance in 1893, another Victorian comedy, revolving around the spectre of illegitimate births, mistaken identities and late revelations. Wilde was commissioned to write two more plays and An Ideal Husband, written in 1894, followed in January 1895.

Peter Raby said these essentially English plays were well-pitched: "Wilde, with one eye on the dramatic genius of Ibsen, and the other on the commercial competition in London's West End, targeted his audience with adroit precision".

Queensberry family

In mid-1891 Lionel Johnson introduced Wilde to Lord Alfred Douglas, Johnson's cousin and an undergraduate at Oxford at the time. Known to his family and friends as "Bosie", he was a handsome and spoilt young man. An intimate friendship sprang up between Wilde and Douglas and by 1893 Wilde was infatuated with Douglas and they consorted together regularly in a tempestuous affair. If Wilde was relatively indiscreet, even flamboyant, in the way he acted, Douglas was reckless in public. Wilde, who was earning up to £100 a week from his plays (his salary at The Woman's World had been £6) indulged Douglas's every whim: material, artistic or sexual.

Douglas soon initiated Wilde into the Victorian underground of gay prostitution and Wilde was introduced to a series of young working-class male prostitutes from 1892 onwards by Alfred Taylor. These infrequent rendezvous usually took the same form: Wilde would meet the boy, offer him gifts, dine him privately and then take him to a hotel room. Unlike Wilde's idealised relations with Ross, John Gray, and Douglas, all of whom remained part of his aesthetic circle, these consorts were uneducated and knew nothing of literature. Soon his public and private lives had become sharply divided; in De Profundis he wrote to Douglas that "It was like feasting with panthers; the danger was half the excitement... I did not know that when they were to strike at me it was to be at another's piping and at another's pay."

Douglas and some Oxford friends founded a journal, The Chameleon, to which Wilde "sent a page of paradoxes originally destined for the Saturday Review". "Phrases and Philosophies for the Use of the Young" was to come under attack six months later at Wilde's trial, where he was forced to defend the magazine to which he had sent his work.In any case, it became unique: The Chameleon was not published again.

Lord Alfred's father, the Marquess of Queensberry, was known for his outspoken atheism, brutish manner and creation of the modern rules of boxing. Queensberry, who feuded regularly with his son, confronted Wilde and Lord Alfred about the nature of their relationship several times, but Wilde was able to mollify him. In June 1894, he called on Wilde at 16 Tite Street, without an appointment, and clarified his stance: "I do not say that you are it, but you look it, and pose at it, which is just as bad. And if I catch you and my son again in any public restaurant I will thrash you" to which Wilde responded: "I don't know what the Queensberry rules are, but the Oscar Wilde rule is to shoot on sight".His account in De Profundis was less triumphant: "It was when, in my library at Tite Street, waving his small hands in the air in epileptic fury, your father... stood uttering every foul word his foul mind could think of, and screaming the loathsome threats he afterwards with such cunning carried out". Queensberry only described the scene once, saying Wilde had "shown him the white feather", meaning he had acted in a cowardly way. Though trying to remain calm, Wilde saw that he was becoming ensnared in a brutal family quarrel. He did not wish to bear Queensberry's insults, but he knew to confront him could lead to disaster were his liaisons disclosed publicly.

The Importance of Being Earnest

Wilde's final play again returns to the theme of switched identities: the play's two protagonists engage in "bunburying" (the maintenance of alternative personas in the town and country) which allows them to escape Victorian social mores.Earnest is even lighter in tone than Wilde's earlier comedies. While their characters often rise to serious themes in moments of crisis, Earnest lacks the by-now stock Wildean characters: there is no "woman with a past", the principals are neither villainous nor cunning, simply idle cultivés, and the idealistic young women are not that innocent. Mostly set in drawing rooms and almost completely lacking in action or violence, Earnest lacks the self-conscious decadence found in The Picture of Dorian Gray and Salome.

The play, now considered Wilde's masterpiece, was rapidly written in Wilde's artistic maturity in late 1894. It was first performed on 14 February 1895, at St James's Theatre in London, Wilde's second collaboration with George Alexander, the actor-manager. Both author and producer assiduously revised, prepared and rehearsed every line, scene and setting in the months before the premiere, creating a carefully constructed representation of late-Victorian society, yet simultaneously mocking it. During rehearsal Alexander requested that Wilde shorten the play from four acts to three, which the author did. Premieres at St James's seemed like "brilliant parties", and the opening of The Importance of Being Earnest was no exception. Allan Aynesworth (who played Algernon) recalled to Hesketh Pearson, "In my fifty-three years of acting, I never remember a greater triumph than [that] first night."Earnest's immediate reception as Wilde's best work to date finally crystallised his fame into a solid artistic reputation. The Importance of Being Earnest remains his most popular play.

Wilde's professional success was mirrored by an escalation in his feud with Queensberry. Queensberry had planned to insult Wilde publicly by throwing a bouquet of rotting vegetables onto the stage; Wilde was tipped off and had Queensberry barred from entering the theatre.Fifteen weeks later Wilde was in prison.

Trials

Wilde v. Queensberry

On 18 February 1895, the Marquess left his calling card at Wilde's Club, the Albemarle, inscribed: "For Oscar Wilde, posing somdomite" Wilde, encouraged by Douglas and against the advice of his friends, initiated a private prosecution against Queensberry for libel, since the note amounted to a public accusation that Wilde had committed the crime of sodomy.

Queensberry was arrested for criminal libel; a charge carrying a possible sentence of up to two years in prison. Under the 1843 Libel Act, Queensberry could avoid conviction for libel only by demonstrating that his accusation was in fact true, and furthermore that there was some "public benefit" to having made the accusation openly. Queensberry's lawyers thus hired private detectives to find evidence of Wilde's homosexual liaisons.

Wilde's friends had advised him against the prosecution at a Saturday Review meeting at the Café Royal on 24 March 1895; Frank Harris warned him that "they are going to prove sodomy against you" and advised him to flee to France. Wilde and Douglas walked out in a huff, Wilde saying "it is at such moments as these that one sees who are one's true friends". The scene was witnessed by George Bernard Shaw who recalled it to Arthur Ransome a day or so before Ransome's trial for libelling Douglas in 1913. To Ransome it confirmed what he had said in his 1912 book on Wilde; that Douglas's rivalry for Wilde with Robbie Ross and his arguments with his father had resulted in Wilde's public disaster; as Wilde wrote in De Profundis. Douglas lost his case. Shaw included an account of the argument between Harris, Douglas and Wilde in the preface to his play The Dark Lady of the Sonnets.

The libel trial became a cause célèbre as salacious details of Wilde's private life with Taylor and Douglas began to appear in the press. A team of private detectives had directed Queensberry's lawyers, led by Edward Carson QC, to the world of the Victorian underground. Wilde's association with blackmailers and male prostitutes, cross-dressers and homosexual brothels was recorded, and various persons involved were interviewed, some being coerced to appear as witnesses since they too were accomplices to the crimes of which Wilde was accused.

The trial opened on 3 April 1895 before Justice Richard Henn Collin amid scenes of near hysteria both in the press and the public galleries. Th extent of the evidence massed against Wilde forced him to declare meekl "I am the prosecutor in this case"Wilde's lawyer, Sir Edward George Clark opened the case by pre-emptively asking Wilde about two suggestive lette Wilde had written to Douglas, which the defence had in its possession. H characterised the first as a "prose sonnet" and admitted that the "poetic language" might seem strange to the court but claimed its intent was innocen Wilde stated that the letters had been obtained by blackmailers who ha attempted to extort money from him, but he had refused, suggesting the should take the £60 (equal to £6,800 today) offered, "unusual for a pros piece of that length". He claimed to regard the letters as works of art rathe than something of which to be ashamed.

Carson, a fellow Dubliner who had attended Trinity College, Dublin a the same time as Wilde, cross-examined Wilde on how he perceived the mora content of his works. Wilde replied with characteristic wit and flippanc claiming that works of art are not capable of being moral or immoral bu only well or poorly made, and that only "brutes and illiterates", whose view on art "are incalculably stupid", would make such judgements about ar Carson, a leading barrister, diverged from the normal practice of asking close questions. Carson pressed Wilde on each topic from every angle, squeezin out nuances of meaning from Wilde's answers, removing them from thei aesthetic context and portraying Wilde as evasive and decadent. While Wild won the most laughs from the court, Carson scored the most legal point To undermine Wilde's credibility, and to justify Queensberry's description c Wilde as a "posing somdomite", Carson drew from the witness an admissio of his capacity for "posing", by demonstrating that he had lied about hi age on oath. Playing on this, he returned to the topic throughout his cross examination. Carson also tried to justify Queensberry's characterisatio by quoting from Wilde's novel, The Picture of Dorian Gray, referring i particular to a scene in the second chapter, in which Lord Henry Wotto explains his decadent philosophy to Dorian, an "innocent young man", i Carson's words.

Carson then moved to the factual evidence and questioned Wilde about his friendships with younger, lower-class men. Wilde admitted being on a first-name basis and lavishing gifts upon them, but insisted that nothing untoward had occurred and that the men were merely good friends of his. Carson repeatedly pointed out the unusual nature of these relationships and insinuated that the men were prostitutes. Wilde replied that he did not believe in social barriers, and simply enjoyed the society of young men. Then Carson asked Wilde directly whether he had ever kissed a certain servant boy, Wilde responded, "Oh, dear no. He was a particularly plain boy – unfortunately ugly – I pitied him for it." Carson pressed him on the answer, repeatedly asking why the boy's ugliness was relevant. Wilde hesitated, then for the first time became flustered: "You sting me and insult me and try to unnerve me; and at times one says things flippantly when one ought to speak more seriously."

In his opening speech for the defence, Carson announced that he had located several male prostitutes who were to testify that they had had sex with Wilde. On the advice of his lawyers, Wilde dropped the prosecution. Queensberry was found not guilty, as the court declared that his accusation that Wilde was "posing as a Somdomite " was justified, "true in substance and in fact".Under the Libel Act 1843, Queensberry's acquittal rendered Wilde legally liable for the considerable expenses Queensberry had incurred in his defence, which left Wilde bankrupt.

Regina v. Wilde

After Wilde left the court, a warrant for his arrest was applied for on charges of sodomy and gross indecency. Robbie Ross found Wilde at the Cadogan Hotel, Pont Street, Knightsbridge, with Reginald Turner; both men advised Wilde to go at once to Dover and try to get a boat to France; his mother advised him to stay and fight. Wilde, lapsing into inaction, could only say, "The train has gone. It's too late."On 6 April 1895, Wilde was arrested for "gross indecency" under Section 11 of the Criminal Law Amendment Act 1885, a term meaning homosexual acts not amounting to buggery (an offence under a separate statute). At Wilde's instruction, Ross and Wilde's butler forced their way into the bedroom and library of 16 Tite Street, packing some personal effects, manuscripts, and letters. Wilde was then imprisoned on remand at Holloway, where he received daily visits from Douglas.

Events moved quickly and his prosecution opened on 26 April 1895, before Mr Justice Charles. Wilde pleaded not guilty. He had already begged Douglas to leave London for Paris, but Douglas complained bitterly, even wanting to give evidence; he was pressed to go and soon fled to the Hotel du Monde. Fearing persecution, Ross and many others also left the United Kingdom during this time. Under cross examination Wilde was at first hesitant, then spoke eloquently:

Charles Gill (prosecuting): What is "the love that dare not speak its name"?

Wilde: "The love that dare not speak its name" in this century is such a great affection of an elder for a younger man as there was between David and Jonathan, such as Plato made the very basis of his philosophy, and such as you find in the sonnets of Michelangelo and Shakespeare. It is that deep spiritual affection that is as pure as it is perfect. It dictates and pervades great works of art, like those of Shakespeare and Michelangelo, and those two letters of mine, such as they are. It is in this century misunderstood, so much misunderstood that it may be described as "the love that dare not speak its name", and on that account of it I am placed where I am now. It is beautiful, it is fine, it is the noblest form of affection. There is nothing unnatural about it. It is intellectual, and it repeatedly exists between an older and a younger man, when the older man has intellect, and the younger man has all the joy, hope and glamour of life before him. That it should be so, the world does not understand. The world mocks at it, and sometimes puts one in the pillory for it.

This response was counter-productive in a legal sense as it only served to reinforce the charges of homosexual behaviour.

The trial ended with the jury unable to reach a verdict. Wilde's counsel, Sir Edward Clarke, was finally able to get a magistrate to allow Wilde and his friends to post bail. The Reverend Stewart Headlam put up most of the £5,000 surety required by the court, having disagreed with Wilde's treatment by the press and the courts. Wilde was freed from Holloway and, shunning attention, went into hiding at the house of Ernest and Ada Leverson, two of his firm friends. Edward Carson approached Frank Lockwood QC, the Solicitor General and asked "Can we not let up on the fellow now?" Lockwood answered that he would like to do so, but feared that the case had become too politicised to be dropped.

The final trial was presided over by Mr Justice Wills. On 25 May 1895 Wilde and Alfred Taylor were convicted of gross indecency and sentenced to two years' hard labour. The judge described the sentence, the maximum allowed, as "totally inadequate for a case such as this", and that the case was "the worst case I have ever tried". Wilde's response "And I? May I say nothing, my Lord?" was drowned out in cries of "Shame" in the courtroom.

Imprisonment

When first I was put into prison some people advised me to try and forget who I was. It was ruinous advice. It is only by realising what I am that I have found comfort of any kind. Now I am advised by others to try on my release to forget that I have ever been in a prison at all. I know that would be equally fatal. It would mean that I would always be haunted by an intolerable sense of disgrace, and that those things that are meant for me as much as for anybody else – the beauty of the sun and moon, the pageant of the seasons, the music of daybreak and the silence of great nights, the rain falling through the leaves, or the dew creeping over the grass and making it silver – would all be tainted for me, and lose their healing power, and their power of communicating joy. To regret one's own experiences is to arrest one's own development. To deny one's own experiences is to put a lie into the lips of one's own life. It is no less than a denial of the soul.

De Profundis

Wilde was incarcerated from 25 May 1895 to 18 May 1897.

He first entered Newgate Prison in London for processing, then was moved to Pentonville Prison, where the "hard labour" to which he had been sentenced consisted of many hours of walking a treadmill and picking oakum (separating the fibres in scraps of old navy ropes), and where prisoners were allowed to read only the Bible and The Pilgrim's Progress.

A few months later he was moved to Wandsworth Prison in London. Inmates there also followed the regimen of "hard labour, hard fare and a hard bed", which wore harshly on Wilde's delicate health. In November he collapsed during chapel from illness and hunger. His right ear drum was ruptured in the fall, an injury that later contributed to his death. He spent two months in the infirmary.

Richard B. Haldane, the Liberal MP and reformer, visited Wilde and had him transferred in November to Reading Gaol, 30 miles (48 km) west of London on 23 November 1895. The transfer itself was the lowest point of his incarceration, as a crowd jeered and spat at him on the railway platform. He spent the remainder of his sentence there, addressed and identified only as "C33" – the occupant of the third cell on the third floor of C ward.

About five months after Wilde arrived at Reading Gaol, Charles Thomas Wooldridge, a trooper in the Royal Horse Guards, was brought to Reading to await his trial for murdering his wife on 29 March 1896; on 17 June Wooldridge was sentenced to death and returned to Reading for his execution, which took place on Tuesday, 7 July 1896 – the first hanging at Reading in 18 years. From Wooldridge's hanging, Wilde later wrote The Ballad of Reading Gaol.

Wilde was not, at first, even allowed paper and pen but Haldane eventually succeeded in allowing access to books and writing materials. Wilde requested, among others: the Bible in French; Italian and German grammars; some Ancient Greek texts, Dante's Divine Comedy, Joris-Karl Huysmans's new French novel about Christian redemption En route, and essays by St Augustine, Cardinal Newman and Walter Pater.

Between January and March 1897 Wilde wrote a 50,000-word letter to Douglas. He was not allowed to send it, but was permitted to take it with him when released from prison. In reflective mode, Wilde coldly examines his career to date, how he had been a colourful agent provocateur in Victorian society, his art, like his paradoxes, seeking to subvert as well as sparkle. His own stimation of himself was: one who "stood in symbolic relations to the art and ulture of my age". It was from these heights that his life with Douglas began, nd Wilde examines that particularly closely, repudiating him for what Wilde nally sees as his arrogance and vanity: he had not forgotten Douglas' remark, when he was ill, "When you are not on your pedestal you are not interesting." Wilde blamed himself, though, for the ethical degradation of character that e allowed Douglas to bring about in him and took responsibility for his wn fall, "I am here for having tried to put your father in prison." The first alf concludes with Wilde forgiving Douglas, for his own sake as much as Douglas's. The second half of the letter traces Wilde's spiritual journey of edemption and fulfilment through his prison reading. He realised that his rdeal had filled his soul with the fruit of experience, however bitter it tasted t the time.

> ... I wanted to eat of the fruit of all the trees in the garden of the world ... And so, indeed, I went out, and so I lived. My only mistake was that I confined myself so exclusively to the trees of what seemed to me the sun-lit side of the garden, and shunned the other side for its shadow and its gloom.

Wilde was released from prison on 19 May 1897 and sailed that evening or Dieppe, France. He never returned to the UK.

On his release, he gave the manuscript to Ross, who may or may not ave carried out Wilde's instructions to send a copy to Douglas (who later enied having received it). The letter was partially published in 1905 as De 'rofundis; its complete and correct publication first occurred in 1962 in The etters of Oscar Wilde.

Decline: 1897–1900

Exile

Though Wilde's health had suffered greatly from the harshness and diet f prison, he had a feeling of spiritual renewal. He immediately wrote to the ociety of Jesus requesting a six-month Catholic retreat; when the request was enied, Wilde wept. "I intend to be received into the Catholic Church before ong", Wilde told a journalist who asked about his religious intentions.

He spent his last three years impoverished and in exile. He took th name "Sebastian Melmoth", after Saint Sebastian and the titular character of Melmoth the Wanderer (a Gothic novel by Charles Maturin, Wilde's great uncle). Wilde wrote two long letters to the editor of the Daily Chronicle describing the brutal conditions of English prisons and advocating penal reform. His discussion of the dismissal of Warder Martin for giving biscuit to an anaemic child prisoner repeated the themes of the corruption and degeneration of punishment that he had earlier outlined in The Soul of Man under Socialism.

Wilde spent mid-1897 with Robert Ross in the seaside village of Berneval-le-Grand in northern France, where he wrote The Ballad of Reading Gaol, narrating the execution of Charles Thomas Wooldridge, who murdered his wife in a rage at her infidelity. It moves from an objective story-telling to symbolic identification with the prisoners. No attempt is made to assess the justice of the laws which convicted them but rather the poem highlights the brutalisation of the punishment that all convicts share. Wilde juxtaposed the executed man and himself with the line "Yet each man kills the thing he loves". He adopted the proletarian ballad form and the author was credited as "C33", Wilde's cell number in Reading Gaol. He suggested that it be published in Reynolds' Magazine, "because it circulates widely among the criminal classes – to which I now belong – for once I will be read by my peer – a new experience for me". It was an immediate roaring commercial success going through seven editions in less than two years, only after which "[Oscar was added to the title page, though many in literary circles had known Wilde to be the author. It brought him a small amount of money.

Although Douglas had been the cause of his misfortunes, he and Wilde were reunited in August 1897 at Rouen. This meeting was disapproved of by the friends and families of both men. Constance Wilde was already refusing to meet Wilde or allow him to see their sons, though she sent him money – three pounds a week. During the latter part of 1897, Wilde and Douglas lived together near Naples for a few months until they were separated by their families under the threat of cutting off all funds.

Wilde's final address was at the dingy Hôtel d'Alsace (now known as L'Hôtel), on rue des Beaux-Arts in Saint-Germain-des-Prés, Paris. "This poverty really breaks one's heart: it is so sale , so utterly depressing, so hopeless. Pray do what you can" he wrote to his publisher.He corrected and published An Ideal Husband and The Importance of Being Earnest, the proofs of which, according to Ellmann, show a man "very much in command of himself and of the play" but he refused to write anything else: "I can write, but have lost the joy of writing".

He wandered the boulevards alone and spent what little money he had on alcohol. A series of embarrassing chance encounters with hostile English visitors, or Frenchmen he had known in better days, drowned his spirit. Soon Wilde was sufficiently confined to his hotel to joke, on one of his final trips outside, "My wallpaper and I are fighting a duel to the death. One of us has got to go". On 12 October 1900 he sent a telegram to Ross: "Terribly weak. Please come". His moods fluctuated; Max Beerbohm relates how their mutual friend Reginald 'Reggie' Turner had found Wilde very depressed after a nightmare. "I dreamt that I had died, and was supping with the dead!" "I am sure", Turner replied, "that you must have been the life and soul of the party."Turner was one of the few of the old circle who remained with Wilde to the end and was at his bedside when he died.

Death

By 25 November 1900 Wilde had developed meningitis, then called "cerebral meningitis". Robbie Ross arrived on 29 November, sent for a priest, and Wilde was conditionally baptised into the Catholic Church by Fr Cuthbert Dunne, a Passionist priest from Dublin,Wilde having been baptised in the Church of Ireland and having moreover a recollection of Catholic baptism as a child, a fact later attested to by the minister of the sacrament, Fr Lawrence Fox.Fr Dunne recorded the baptism,

As the voiture rolled through the dark streets that wintry night, the sad story of Oscar Wilde was in part repeated to me... Robert Ross knelt by the bedside, assisting me as best he could while I administered conditional baptism, and afterwards answering the responses while I gave Extreme Unction to the prostrate man and recited the prayers for the dying. As the man was in a semi-comatose condition, I did not venture to administer the Holy Viaticum; still I must add that he could be roused and was roused from this state in my presence. When roused he gave signs of being inwardly conscious... Indeed I was fully satisfied that he understood me when told that I was about to receive him into the Catholic Church and gave him the Last Sacraments... And when repeated close to his ear the Holy Names, the Acts of Contrition, Faith Hope and Charity, with acts of humble resignation to the Will of God he tried all through to say the words after me.

Wilde died of meningitis on 30 November 1900. Different opinions are given as to the cause of the disease: Richard Ellmann claimed it was syphilitic Merlin Holland, Wilde's grandson, thought this to be a misconception noting that Wilde's meningitis followed a surgical intervention, perhaps a mastoidectomy; Wilde's physicians, Dr Paul Cleiss and A'Court Tucker reported that the condition stemmed from an old suppuration of the right ear (from the prison injury, see above) treated for several years (une ancienne suppuration de l'oreille droite d'ailleurs en traitement depuis plusieurs années, and made no allusion to syphilis.

Burial

Wilde was initially buried in the Cimetière de Bagneux outside Paris; in 1909 his remains were disinterred and transferred to Père Lachaise Cemetery inside the city. His tomb there was designed by Sir Jacob Epstein. It was commissioned by Robert Ross, who asked for a small compartment to be made for his own ashes, which were duly transferred in 1950. The modernist angel depicted as a relief on the tomb was originally complete with male genitalia which were initially censored by French Authorities with a golden leaf. The genitals have since been vandalised; their current whereabouts are unknown. In 2000, Leon Johnson, a multimedia artist, installed a silver prosthesis to replace them. In 2011, the tomb was cleaned of the many lipstick marks left there by admirers and a glass barrier was installed to prevent further marks or damage.

The epitaph is a verse from The Ballad of Reading Gaol,

> And alien tears will fill for him
>
> Pity's long-broken urn,
>
> For his mourners will be outcast men,
>
> And outcasts always mourn.

Posthumous pardon

In 2017, Wilde was among an estimated 50,000 men who were pardoned for homosexual acts that were no longer considered offences under the Policing and Crime Act 2017. The Act is known informally as the Alan Turing law.

Honours

In 2014 Wilde was one of the inaugural honorees in the Rainbow Honor Walk, a walk of fame in San Francisco's Castro neighbourhood noting LGBTQ people who have "made significant contributions in their fields."

Biographies

Wilde's life has been the subject of numerous biographies since his death. The earliest were memoirs by those who knew him: often they are personal or impressionistic accounts which can be good character sketches, but are sometimes factually unreliable. Frank Harris, his friend and editor, wrote a biography, Oscar Wilde: His Life and Confessions (1916); though prone to exaggeration and sometimes factually inaccurate, it offers a good literary portrait of Wilde. Lord Alfred Douglas wrote two books about his relationship with Wilde. Oscar Wilde and Myself (1914), largely ghost-written by T. W. H. Crosland, vindictively reacted to Douglas's discovery that De Profundis was addressed to him and defensively tried to distance him from Wilde's scandalous reputation. Both authors later regretted their work. Later, in Oscar Wilde: A Summing Up (1939) and his Autobiography he was more sympathetic to Wilde. Of Wilde's other close friends, Robert Sherard; Robert Ross, his literary executor; and Charles Ricketts variously published biographies, reminiscences or correspondence. The first more or less objective biography of Wilde came about when Hesketh Pearson wrote Oscar Wilde: His Life and Wit (1946). In 1954 Wilde's son Vyvyan Holland published his memoir Son of Oscar Wilde, which recounts the difficulties Wilde's wife and children faced after his imprisonment. It was revised and updated by Merlin Holland in 1989.

Oscar Wilde, a critical study by Arthur Ransome was published in 1912. The book only briefly mentioned Wilde's life, but subsequently Ransome (and The Times Book Club) were sued for libel by Lord Alfred Douglas. In April 1913 Douglas lost the libel action after a reading of De Profundis refuted his claims.

Richard Ellmann wrote his 1987 biography Oscar Wilde, for which he posthumously won a National (USA) Book Critics Circle Award in 1988 and a Pulitzer Prize in 1989. The book was the basis for the 1997 film Wilde, directed by Brian Gilbert and starring Stephen Fry as the title character.

Neil McKenna's 2003 biography, The Secret Life of Oscar Wilde, offers an exploration of Wilde's sexuality. Often speculative in nature, it was widely criticised for its pure conjecture and lack of scholarly rigour. Thomas Wright's Oscar's Books (2008) explores Wilde's reading from his childhood in Dublin to his death in Paris. After tracking down many books that once belonged to Wilde's Tite Street library (dispersed at the time of his trials), Wright was the first to examine Wilde's marginalia.

> Later on, I think everyone will recognise his achievements; his plays and essays will endure. Of course, you may think with others that his personality and conversation were far more wonderful than anything he wrote, so that his written works give only a pale reflection of his power. Perhaps that is so, and of course, it will be impossible to reproduce what is gone forever.

Robert Ross, 23 December 1900

In 2018, Matthew Sturgis' "Oscar: A Life," was published in London. The book incorporates rediscovered letters and other documents and is the most extensively researched biography of Wilde to appear since 1988.

Parisian literati, also produced several biographies and monographs on im. André Gide wrote In Memoriam, Oscar Wilde and Wilde also features his journals. Thomas Louis, who had earlier translated books on Wilde into French, produced his own L'esprit d'Oscar Wilde in 1920. Modern books include Philippe Jullian's Oscar Wilde, and L'affaire Oscar Wilde, ou, Du danger de laisser la justice mettre le nez dans nos draps (The Oscar Wilde Affair, or, On the Danger of Allowing Justice to put its Nose in our Sheets) by Odon Vallet, a French religious historian. (Source: Wikipedia)

NOTABLE WORKS

ESSAYS

"The Decay of Lying" First published in Nineteenth Century (1889) republished in Intentions (1891).

"Pen, Pencil and Poison" First published in the Fortnightly Review (1889), republished in Intentions (1891).

"The Soul of Man under Socialism" First published in the Fortnightly Review (1891), republished in The Soul of Man (1895), privately printed.

Intentions (1891) Wilde revised his dialogues on aesthetic subjects for publication in this volume, which comprises:

- "The Critic as Artist"
- "The Decay of Lying"
- "Pen, Pencil and Poison"
- "The Truth of Masks"

"Phrases and Philosophies for the Use of the Young" first published in the Oxford student magazine The Chameleon, December 1894)

"A Few Maxims For The Instruction Of The Over-Educated" First published, anonymously, in the 1894 November 17 issue of Saturday Review

FICTION

Novel

The Picture of Dorian Gray (1890/1891). The first version of "The Picture of Dorian Gray" was published, in a form highly edited by the magazine, as the lead story in the July 1890 edition of Lippincott's Monthly Magazine. Wilde published the longer and revised version in book form in 1891, with an added preface.

Stories

"The Portrait of Mr. W. H." (1889)

The Happy Prince and Other Tales (1888, a collection of fairy tales) consisting of:

- "The Happy Prince"
- "The Nightingale and the Rose"
- "The Selfish Giant"
- "The Devoted Friend"
- "The Remarkable Rocket"

A House of Pomegranates (1891, fairy tales)

Lord Arthur Savile's Crime and Other Stories (1891) Including "The Canterville Ghost" first published in periodical form in 1887.

Complete Short Fiction. Penguin Classics, 2003. Edited with an Introduction and Notes by Ian Small. Contains all works listed above plus Poems in Prose (1894) and one very short 'Elder-tree' (fragment).

<u>**POEMS**</u>

Ravenna (1878) Winner of the Newdigate Prize.

Poems (1881) Wilde's collection of poetry and first publication.

The Sphinx (1894)

Poems in Prose (1894)

The Ballad of Reading Gaol (1898)

PLAYS

Vera; or, The Nihilists (1880)

The Duchess of Padua (1883)

Lady Windermere's Fan (1892)

A Woman of No Importance (1893)

Salomé (French version) (1893, first performed in Paris 1896)

Salomé: A Tragedy in One Act: Translated from the French of Oscar Wilde by Lord Alfred Douglas, illustrated by Aubrey Beardsley (1894)

An Ideal Husband (1895) (text)

The Importance of Being Earnest (1895) (text)

La Sainte Courtisane and A Florentine Tragedy Fragmentary. First published 1908 in Methuen's Collected Works

(Dates are dates of first performance, which approximate better to the probable date of composition than dates of publication.)

The Importance of Being Earnest and Other Plays. Penguin Classics 2000. Edited with an Introduction, Commentaries and Notes by Richard Allen Cave. Contains all from above save the first two. Salome is in English

As an appendix there is one excised scene from The Importance of Being Earnest.

POSTHUMOUS (PREVIOUSLY UNPUBLISHED)

De Profundis (Written 1895-97, in Reading Gaol). Expurgated edition published 1905; suppressed portions 1913, expanded version in The Letters of Oscar Wilde (1962).

The Rise of Historical Criticism (Written while at college) First published in 1905 (Sherwood Press, Hartford, CT) privately printed. Reprinted in Miscellanies, the last volume of the First Collected Edition (1908).

The First Collected Edition (Methuen & Co., 14 volumes) appeared in 1908 and contained many previously unpublished works.

The Second Collected Edition (Methuen & Co., 12 volumes) appeared in installments between 1909–11 and contained several other unpublished works.

The Letters of Oscar Wilde (Written 1868-1900) Published in 1962. Republished as The Complete Letters of Oscar Wilde (2000), with letters discovered since 1962, and new annotations by Merlin Holland.

The Women of Homer (Written 1876, while at college). First published in Oscar Wilde: The Women of Homer (2008) by The Oscar Wilde Society.

The Philosophy of Dress First published in The New-York Tribune (1885), published for the first time in book form in Oscar Wilde On Dress (2013).

MISATTRIBUTED

Teleny, or The Reverse of the Medal (Paris, 1893) has been attributed to Wilde, but its authorship is unclear. One theory is that it was a combined effort by several of Wilde's friends, which he may have edited.

Constance On September 14, 2011, Wilde's grandson Merlin Holland contested Wilde's claimed authorship of this play entitled Constance, scheduled to open that week in the King's Head Theatre. It was not, in fact, "Oscar Wilde's final play," as its producers were claiming. Holland said Wilde did sketch out the play's scenario in 1894, but "never wrote a word" of it, and that "it is dishonest to foist this on the public." The Artistic Director Adam Spreadbury-Maher of the King's Head Theatre and producer of Constance pointed out that Wilde's son, Vyvyan Holland, wrote in 1954, "a significant amount of the dialogue (of Constance) bears the authentic stamp of my father's hand". There is further proof that the developed scenario that Constance was reconstituted from was written by Wilde between 1897 and his death in 1900, rather than the 1894 George Alexander scenario which Merlin Holland quotes.

CPSIA information can be obtained
at www.ICGtesting.com
Printed in the USA
LVHW111923170820
663425LV00016B/575